Standard Grade

Physics

revision notes

6th edition reprinted 2004

ISBN 1-898890-76-5

Published by
Leckie & Leckie Ltd, 8 Whitehill Terrace, St. Andrews, Scotland, KY16 8RN
tel. 01334 475656 fax. 01334 477392
enquiries@leckieandleckie.co.uk www.leckieandleckie.co.uk

Special thanks to
Caleb Rutherford (cover design concept), Bruce Ryan (project management),
Hamish Sanderson (illustration), Cathy Sprent (cover design)

A CIP Catalogue record for this book is available from the British Library.

Leckie & Leckie is a division of Granada Learning Limited, part of ITV plc.

To Bob Neill for his helpful advice and his assistance as a proofreader

To Hamish Sanderson for his artwork and particularly for Stan, the Standard Grade Snake

To Maggie Hutton for her help with Practice Questions

To Richard Bush for his help with this edition.

To Nicole Dewar (proofreading), Bruce Ryan (production) and Eliana Wilson (keying)

Contents

1. Revision Advice

Dear Pupil . . .

Look forward to that fateful day in the summer when your Standard Grade results finally arrive. On that day it will be too late to do anything about them. But, it's not too late today. The time to start doing something about your Physics is **now**!

Let's start with some honest talking. You want to get the best possible results with the least possible work. After all, there are many things in life that are at least as interesting as Physics, like TV, socialising, etc. The formula for success is **organisation.**

Why waste an hour muddling about when you can get the job done in twenty minutes? Organisation means knowing **where** to work, **when** to work and **what** to do.

On the next few pages you will see some advice on working in an organised way. Please don't miss these pages out; they are probably the most important in these notes!

Where to work

1. Try to work in the **same place** every time.

2. Use a **desk** or a **table**.

3. Try working in **silence** – No TV. No radio. No talkative friends!

When to work

1. Look over your day's work **as soon as possible** after you have done it. Don't leave it till 'later' – do it while your memory is still fresh!

2. Try drawing up a timetable for your evenings. Fit in half-hour sessions of school work and allow yourself some time off for relaxation. Something like this:

	6.00 pm		7.00 pm		8.00 pm		9.00 pm		10.00 pm
Monday	Tea		TV		Physics	French	History	Maths	
Tuesday	Tea	Chem.	Swimming				Reading	Bed	
Wednesday	Tea		Maths	Geog.	Eng.	Reading	Chem.	Video	

What to do

(a) For revision

1. **Plan** the session in advance – with about 25 minutes for work followed by a 5 minute break. Research shows that if you know the break is coming up you work better as the end of the 25 minute session approaches.

2. Look over two or three of the numbered items. Read slowly and carefully. Close the notes and ask yourself 'What have I just read?' Answer yourself either aloud or by jotting down some rough notes on a piece of paper.

3. Go back and check over the section again before you go on to the next bit.

4. Try to look at the same section again a day or so later. **Repetition** is a bit boring but it's very effective.

5. Don't just sit and stare silently at the print for hours on end. It really impresses your parents but it's a waste of time!

6. Try to practise answering **questions**, either the ones in these notes or others from past papers and earlier school work. It's really worth the effort trying to get examples of previous papers!

(b) Before the exam

1. About a month before, issue a serious warning to the family not to fuss and get anxious. It won't help you at all.

2. About a week before, take precautions against Murphy's Law. Here are three examples of his famous Law:
   (a) Calculator batteries and pens only wear out in the middle of exams.
   (b) Pencils only break when you don't have a sharpener.
   (c) You will only be required to draw a diagram if you have forgotten your ruler.

(c) In the exam

1. Take the time to read questions slowly. Read them again.

2. Take a look at the marks available and the space available to write in an answer. Use them to judge how much to write.

3. Never miss out a multiple choice question. Come back to it later. Make an informed guess if you have to.

4. Try to relax; breathe slowly; read carefully; think carefully!

2. Practicals

For your final practical grade you will be assessed on two main areas: **Practical Techniques** and **Investigations**.

Practical Techniques

You will have to complete 8 'mini-' practicals called **Techniques**. You either pass or fail; but if you fail, you might get another chance.

- **Practical Techniques Checklist**
You can keep your own check on the number of techniques you have completed. Tick the box once you have successfully completed the experiment.

	Technique	✔		*Technique*	✔
1	Measure the speed of a moving object.		5	Measure current and voltage correctly.	
2	Measure the focal length of a lens.		6	Measure peak voltage of an a.c. supply on an oscilloscope.	
3	Measure angles of incidence and refraction in a glass or plastic block.		7	Set up a voltage divider to obtain a particular voltage.	
4	Detect an open circuit or short circuit.		8	Wire up a mixed series/parallel circuit given a circuit diagram.	

Investigations

You will have to complete two small projects called **Investigations**. Look below at the Investigation Checklist and at the extracts from an Investigation done recently by a pupil. You could use the checklist to help you with your own Investigation.

- **Investigation Checklist**

		✔
Getting started	- Decide what topic to investigate.	
	- What quantities will you measure?	
	- How will you make the measurements?	
	- What is the aim of the investigation?	
	- What is your hypothesis?	
Doing the experiment	- Take care with apparatus. Be safe!	
	- Which variable is the independent variable, the one you change? (The other variable is called the dependent one.)	
	- Any other variable quantities might change and mess up your results. Identify them and keep them constant.	
	- Try to get a wide range of results.	
	- Make several sets of readings if possible and take an average.	

- **Investigation Checklist (cont.)**

		✔
Writing up	- Draw a table of all your results with correct headings and units.	☐
	- Draw a line graph with the two axes correctly labelled. Do it yourself. Don't use a computer.	☐
	- Write your conclusion.	☐
	- Say whether your hypothesis was correct or wrong. If wrong, can you suggest a better one?	☐
	- Make sure to include a description (diagram) of apparatus. Write down clear instructions on how to measure the variables.	☐

Example of an Investigation

Investigation into the strength of an electromagnet
Louisa Smith 4X

- Introduction

Electromagnets are used in car scrapyards to pick up cars. I want to find out how the current in the electromagnet affects its lifting strength.

I am going to find the strength of the electromagnet by measuring the mass it can lift and I am going to measure the electric current in the electromagnet.

The aim of the investigation is to find whether the current affects the mass that can be lifted.

My hypothesis is that as current increases, the mass lifted will increase. The independent variable is the current. (I will change the current using the variable resistor.) The dependent variable is the mass lifted.

- Method

Using this circuit, I can change the current using the variable resistor then read the current on the a.c. ammeter. I will hang small 10 gram pieces of steel on the magnet's core and see what mass it can lift.

I will keep the number of turns of wire in the electromagnet and the core material the same throughout the experiment because they are variables which might also affect the lifting strength.

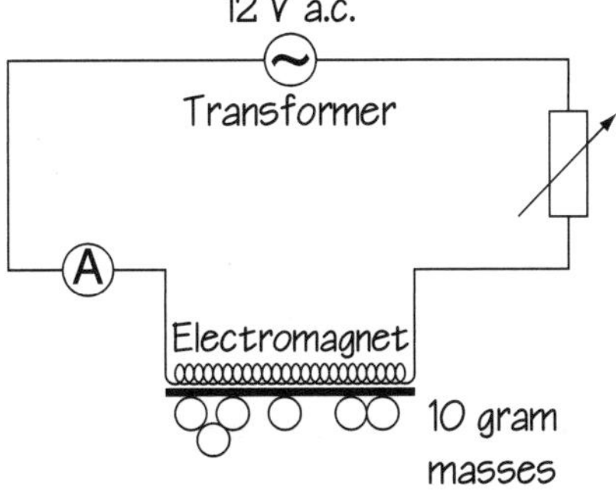

Example of an Investigation (cont.)

- Results

Current (ampères)	Mass lifted (grams)	
	1st reading	2nd reading
0	0	0
1	0	0
2	10	10
3	20	20
4	30	30
5	50	50
6	60	60
7	80	80
8	90	90

I repeated the experiment only once, because there was no change in the readings the second time.

Graph of mass lifted against current for an electromagnet

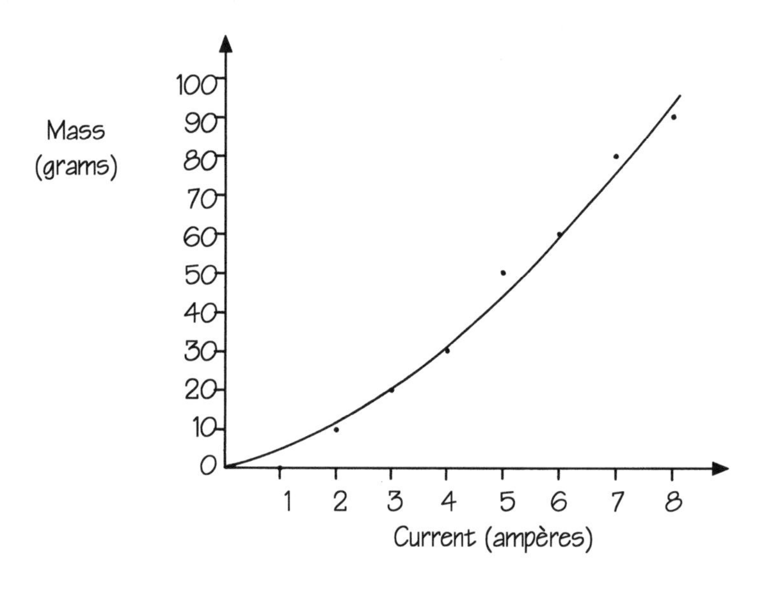

- Conclusion
  The curve of best fit shows that as the current increases, the mass lifted also increases. My hypothesis was correct.

Now go back to the checklist and see if Louisa has covered most of the main points.

Throughout these Notes, Credit level pupils should read **every** item. General level pupils can afford to miss out the extra Credit level work which is printed on a grey background.

3. Telecommunications

Sound

1. The speed of sound in air is approximately 340 metres per second (340 m/s).

2. The speed of light in air or space is 300,000,000 m/s (3×10^8 m/s).

3. Light travels nearly a million times faster than sound.

4. Average speed = $\frac{\text{Distance}}{\text{Time}}$ $v = \frac{d}{t}$

5. Learn up an experiment to measure the speed of sound using the above formula. Here's one:

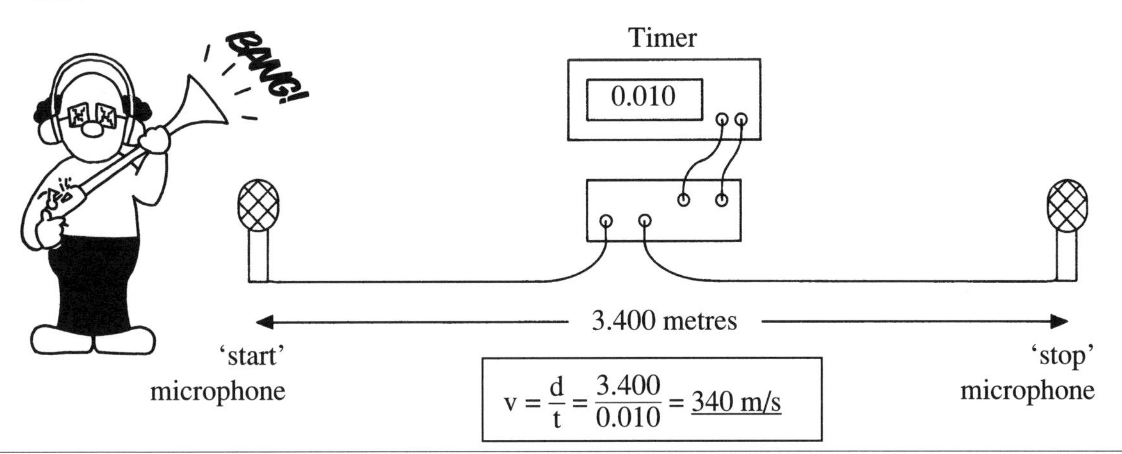

Messages in Wires

1. Here's a simple circuit to send a message along a wire using Morse Code.

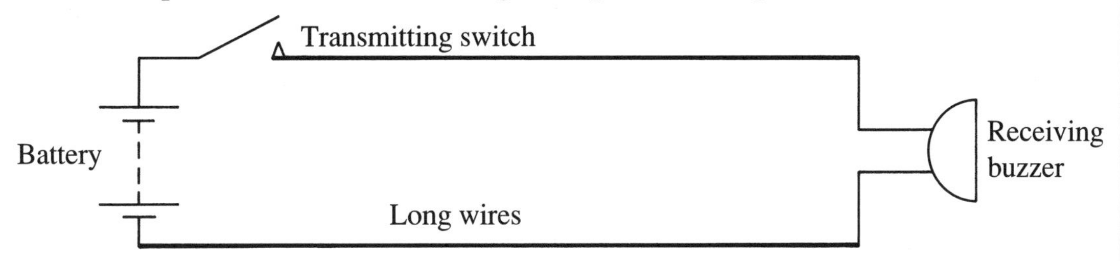

2. Two advantages of using wires rather than using sound in air:
   (a) messages can go farther
   (b) messages can be kept more private.

Messages in Wires (cont.)

3. The telephone is a good example of the benefits mentioned in **2**.

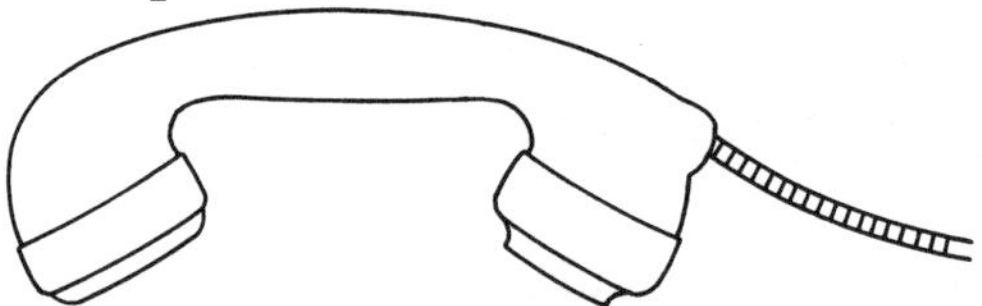

Earpiece is a loudspeaker which changes electrical energy to sound energy.

Mouthpiece is a microphone which changes sound energy to electrical energy.

4. The electrical signals produced by a telephone travel almost as fast as light.

5. Here are some telephone sounds displayed on an oscilloscope.

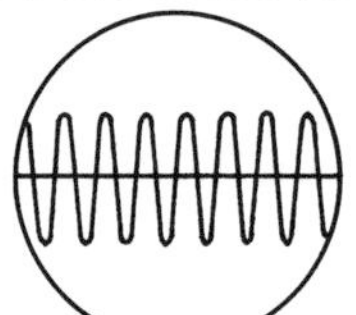

high frequency
(high pitch)

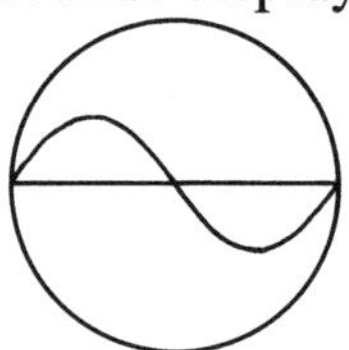

low frequency
(low pitch)

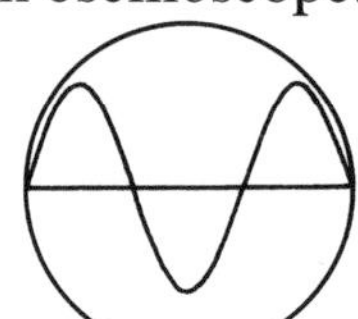

large amplitude
(loud)

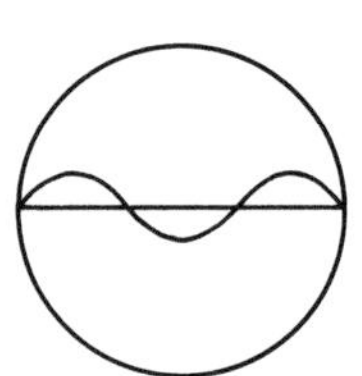

small amplitude
(quiet)

Wave Ideas

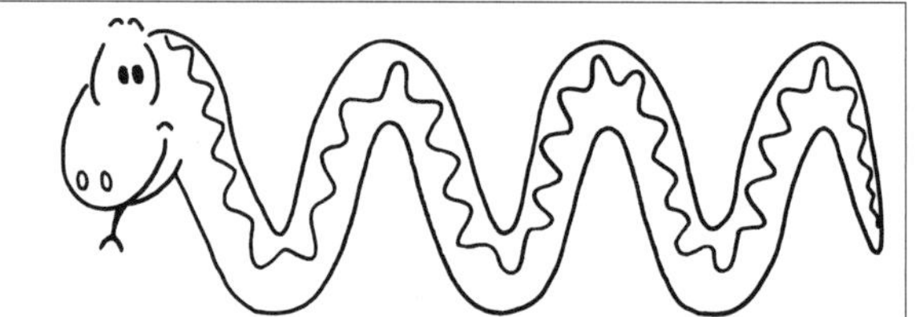

1. Waves can carry signals or messages.

2. Amplitude, a, is the distance from the centre line to the top (or the bottom) of the wave. Amplitude tells you how much energy the wave carries or how strong the signal is.

3. Wavelength, λ (lambda), is the distance between similar points on the wave. Wavelength is usually measured in centimetres or **metres**.

4. Frequency, f, is the number of waves per second. Frequency is measured in **hertz**, Hz. One hertz means one wave every second.

5. Two useful equations: Wave speed = Frequency × Wavelength $v = f\lambda$

$$\text{Wave speed} = \frac{\text{Distance}}{\text{Time}} \qquad v = \frac{d}{t}$$

Radio and TV

1. Radio and TV signals are transmitted as electromagnetic waves which carry energy through air or space at the speed of light (3×10^8 m/s).

   Each station broadcasts on a particular wavelength (or frequency).

2. Make sure you have tried problems using $v = \frac{d}{t}$

   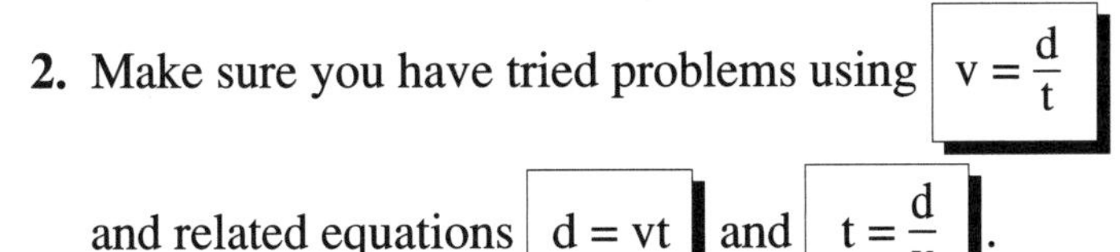

   and related equations $d = vt$ and $t = \frac{d}{v}$.

   The formula isn't too difficult, but you may have to practise using big numbers. Try the following; they all give the same answer:

   $9 \times 10^{14} \div 3 \times 10^2 =$ ☐ $3 \times 10^8 \times 10^4 =$ ☐ $(6 \times 10^{15}) \div (2 \times 10^3) =$ ☐

3. Here are the main parts of a radio receiver. Learn them!

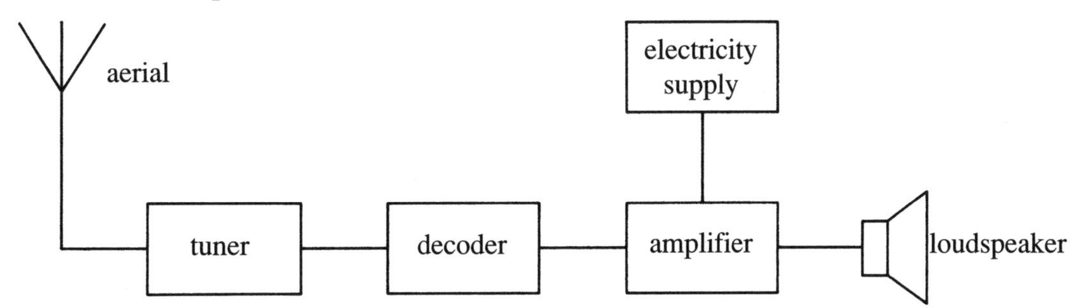

4. The **aerial** picks up waves of many different frequencies and changes them into tiny electric currents.

   The **tuner** (a capacitor and coil) selects one particular frequency.

   The **decoder** (a diode) changes a.c. into d.c. so the signal can eventually be heard on a loudspeaker.

   The **amplifier** increases the electrical energy to make it big enough to operate the loudspeaker.

   The **loudspeaker** changes the electrical energy into sound energy.

   The **electricity supply** provides energy for the amplifier.

Radio and TV (cont.)

5. Amplitude Modulation. Do you understand it?

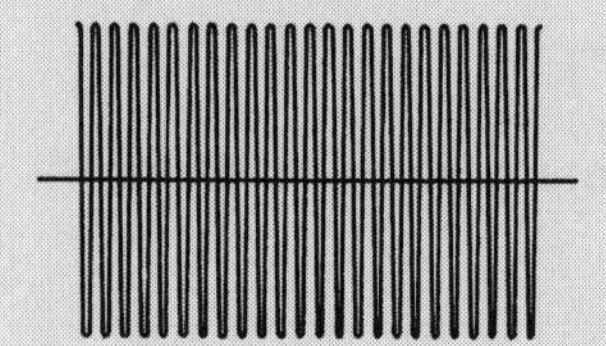

Radio station makes a **carrier wave** at a high radio frequency (e.g. 10^6 Hz).

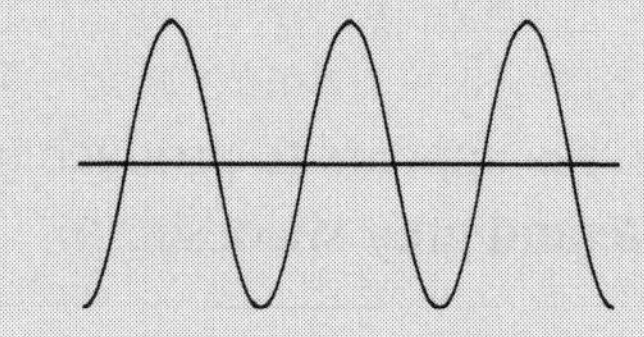

Voice or music at **audio frequency** (e.g. 10^3 Hz) is added to the carrier wave to change its amplitude.

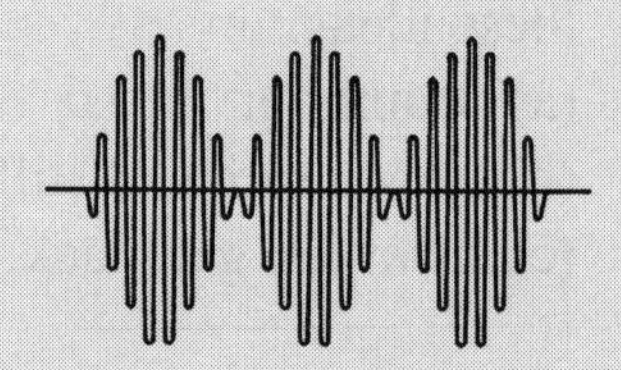

This is the result. The carrier wave has been **amplitude modulated**.

6. Diffraction. Long wavelengths diffract more than short ones, so which waves give better reception in hilly areas?

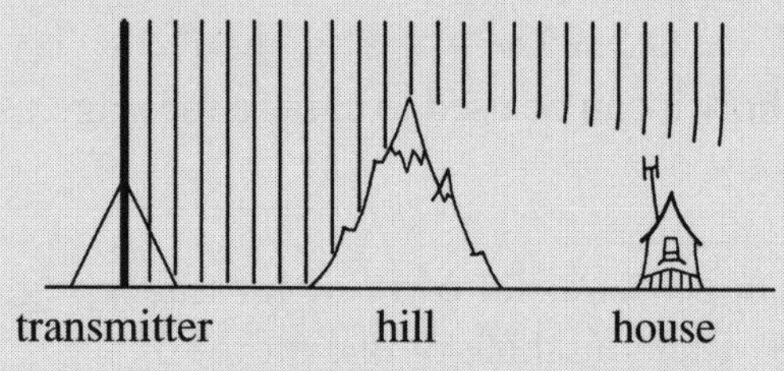

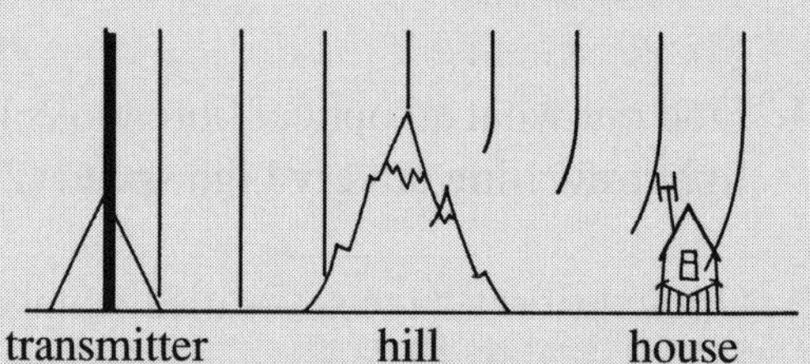

7. Find out a little about different radio frequencies:
How far do UHF and VHF signals travel? About as far as the horizon. They travel in straight lines.

8. Can you identify the main parts of a television receiver?
Complete this block diagram including: video amplifier, sound decoder, picture tube, loudspeaker.

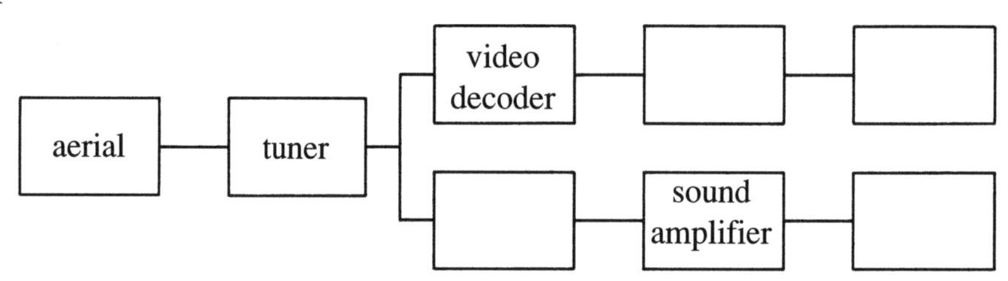

9. Make sure you know what each block does to the signal.

10. Can you describe how a TV signal is transmitted and received?
Key terms are: carrier wave, modulation, video receiver, audio receiver.

11. How is a 625 line TV picture built up? The key word here is **scanning**!

Radio and TV (cont.)

12. Write down a sentence or two about how a black and white TV picture is made up. Include these ideas:
(a) scanning;
(b) how a series of still pictures appears to produce movement (image retention);
(c) how you get black, white and grey shades.

13. All the colours you see on a colour TV can be made from red, green and blue.

14. Red + Green = Yellow Blue + Green = Cyan Red + Blue = Magenta
Red + Blue + Green = White

Fibre Optics

1. Find out what an optical fibre looks like and how it can be used to carry a message using light travelling at very high speed (2×10^8 m/s).

2. Optical fibres have several advantages over copper wires for carrying messages, e.g. the lower cost of glass, no electrical interference. Can you think of one more?

3. Reflection

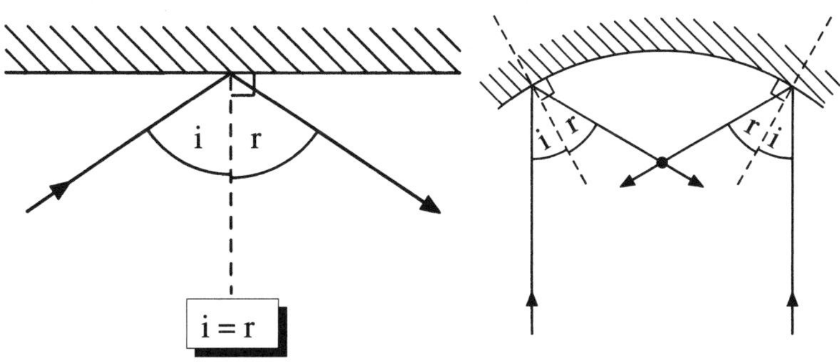

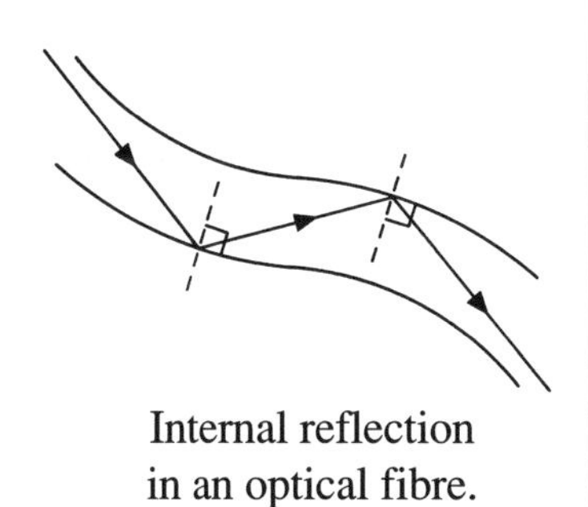

Internal reflection in an optical fibre.

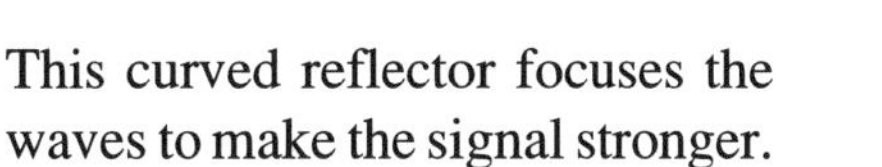

This curved reflector focuses the waves to make the signal stronger.

Satellites

1. The time for one orbit of the Earth is the **period**. The period depends **only** on the height above the Earth.

2. Geostationary satellites have a period of 24 hours. They always stay above the same point on the equator. They can be used to communicate between one continent and another.

3. Satellite signals travel a long way so they become very weak. Curved reflectors can boost a weak signal. The bigger their diameter, the better they work. Can you explain why?

4. Using Electricity

Household Electrics

1. Electricity provides **energy**.

2. Energy can be measured in **joules**, J.

3. Power = $\frac{\text{Energy}}{\text{Time}}$ $P = \frac{E}{t}$

4. Power can be measured in **watts**, W.

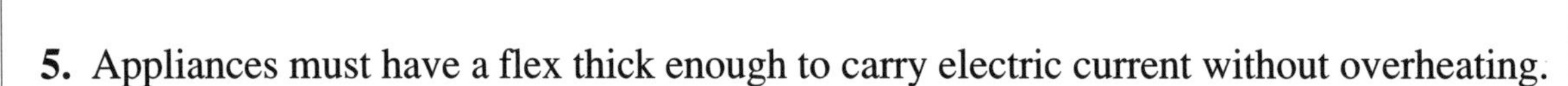

5. Appliances must have a flex thick enough to carry electric current without overheating.

6. The flex and appliance are protected by a fuse in the plug. Two common sizes of fuse are 3 A and 13 A. 3 A fuses can be used for appliances with power ratings up to 700 watts.

7. Examples:

Appliance	*Power (watts)*	*Flex thickness (square millimetres)*	*Suitable fuse (ampères)*
Table lamp	60	0.5	3
Fan heater	2,000	1.0	13

8. Plug wiring:

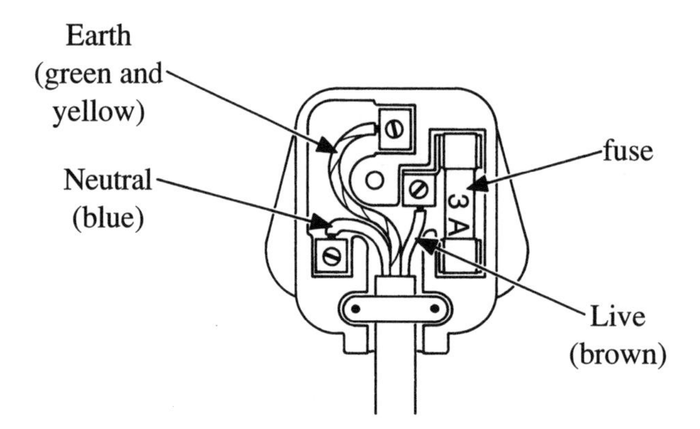

9. Safety checks:
(a) Humans conduct electricity; electricity can kill.
(b) Wet humans conduct electricity much better!!
(c) The earth wire is there for safety.
(d) Appliances which are double insulated don't need an earth wire.
(e) Double insulation symbol. ⧈

Household Electrics (cont.)

10. Check up on things that can go wrong: frayed or worn flexes, too many adaptors in a socket, wrong size of fuse.

11. Make sure you know:
(a) How the earth wire acts as a safety device. If an earthed metal casing accidentally becomes live, then a large current will travel from the live casing to earth and blow the fuse. This cuts off the circuit.
(b) Why fuses and switches are in the live lead and not the neutral lead. Think what would happen in (a) above if there were no fuse in the live lead. The casing would remain live and if you touched it you could receive a shock!

A.C. and D.C.

1. Batteries supply direct current (d.c.). The current always goes in the same direction. It goes from the negative terminal to the positive terminal.

2. Transformers supply alternating current (a.c.). In the UK, the current goes backwards and forwards 50 times every second. We say the frequency is 50 hertz (50 Hz).

3. Oscilloscope wave patterns for d.c. and a.c.

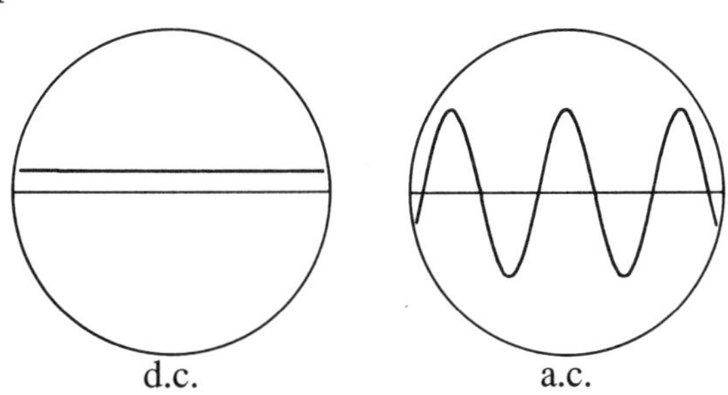

4. The declared value of mains voltage is 230 volts in the UK.

5. The declared value of an a.c. voltage is always less than its peak value. Our mains voltage peaks at about 340 volts.

6. Learn these circuit symbols:

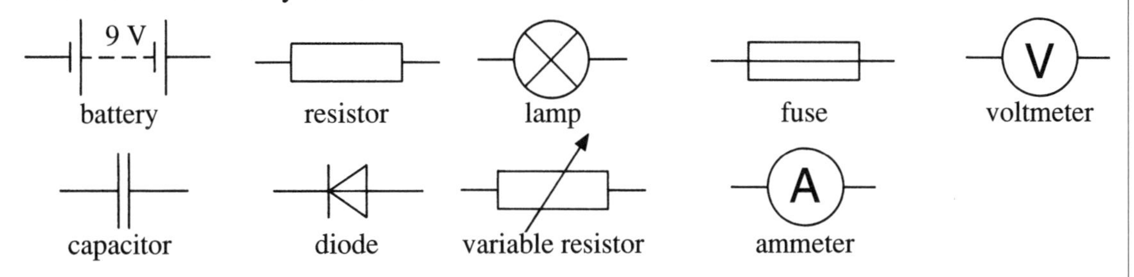

7. An electric current is a drift of electrons through a conductor.

8. Current = $\frac{\text{Charge}}{\text{Time}}$

$$I = \frac{Q}{t}$$

Charge is measured in **coulombs**, C, and time in **seconds**, s.

9. Current is measured in **ampères**, A, using an ammeter placed in series.

A.C. and D.C. (cont.)

10. Voltage is the push or force that moves the electrons and gives them energy.

11. Voltage is measured in **volts**, V, using a voltmeter placed in parallel.

Resistance

1. Resistance = $\frac{\text{Voltage}}{\text{Current}}$ $\qquad R = \frac{V}{I}$

2. The ratio $\frac{V}{I}$ remains constant for a resistor provided it does not heat up.

3. Resistance is measured in **ohms**, Ω.

4. Resistance can be found using the following circuit:

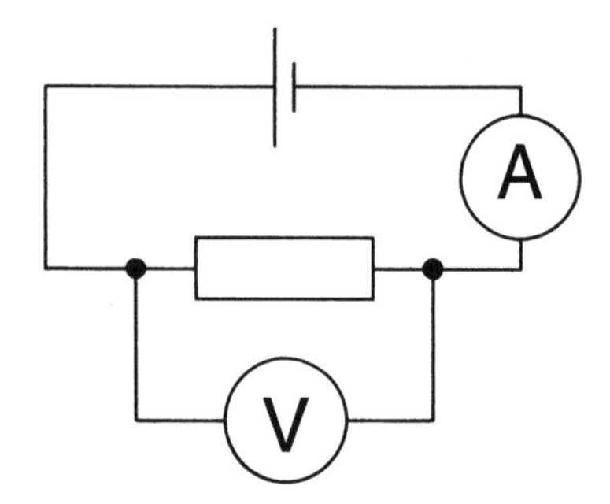

Resistance = $\frac{\text{Voltmeter reading}}{\text{Ammeter reading}}$

5. Variable resistors have many uses, e.g. in the volume control of a radio. Check up on one other use.

6. When there is a current in a wire, electrical energy changes into heat and sometimes light, as in a light bulb. Think of one other example.

7. In a gas discharge tube and a filament lamp electrical energy changes to light. Gas discharge tubes are more efficient because they produce more light and less heat.

8. Power = Voltage × Current $\qquad P = VI$

9. Another useful power formula $\qquad P = I^2R$

Can you prove this formula starting from $P = VI$ and using $V = IR$?

Series and Parallel

1. **Current** is the same at all points in a series circuit.

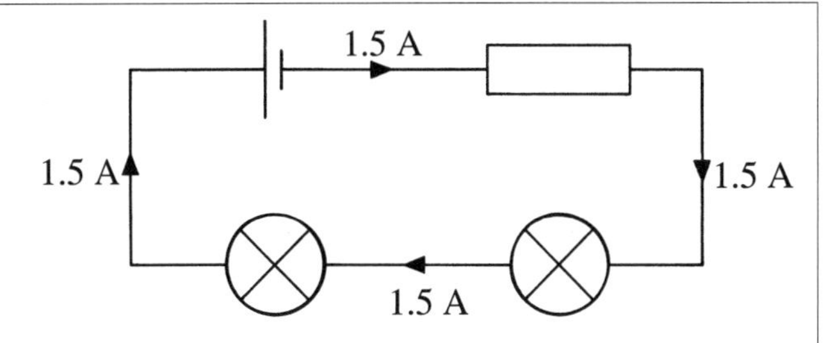

2. 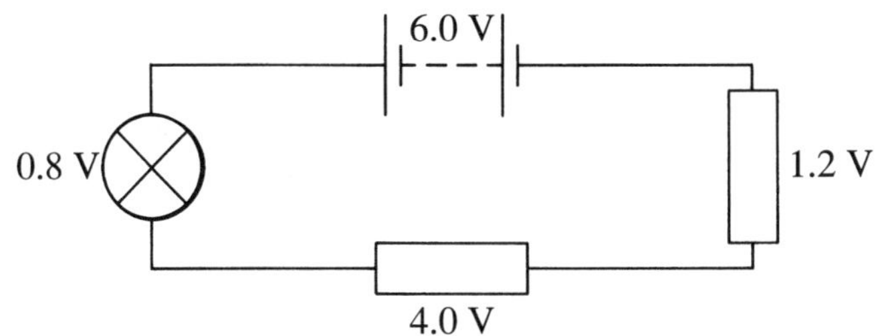

The sum of the voltages in a series circuit equals the supply voltage.

0.8 + 4.0 + 1.2 = <u>6.0 V</u>

3. Find out where you have two switches in series in a circuit in your home.

4. The sum of the currents in the branches of a parallel circuit equals the supply current.

2.0 + 2.0 + 0.5 = <u>4.5 A</u>

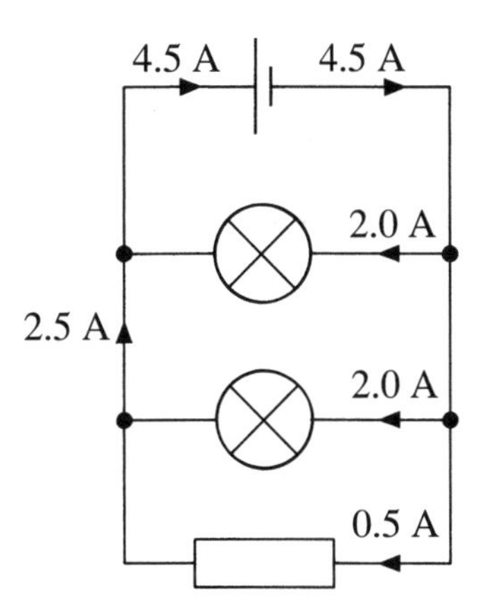

5. If you have too many branches in a parallel circuit the supply current might become very large. This could happen at home if you have too many appliances on one socket.

6. 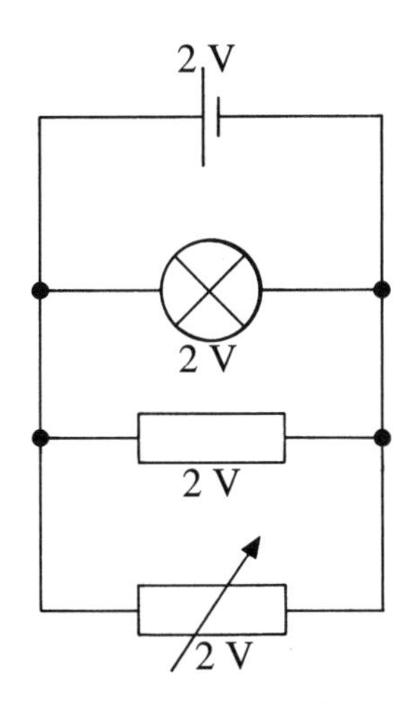

The voltage across each branch of a parallel circuit is the same.

7. Car lighting circuits are parallel circuits. Could you draw a simple diagram?

8. Fault finding. You can test circuits with an ohmmeter Ω or a simple continuity tester

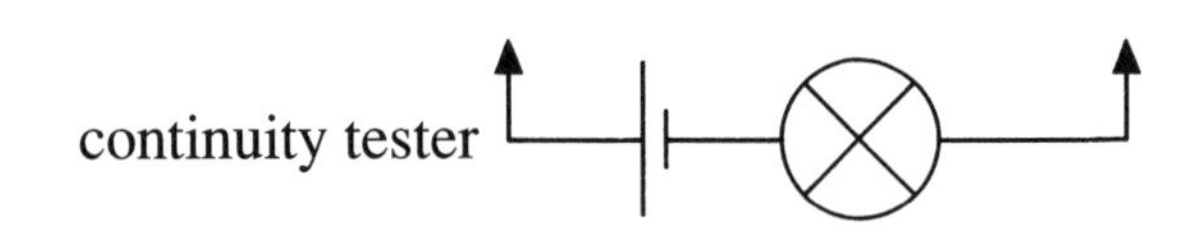

Series and Parallel (cont.)

9. **Open circuits** **Short circuits**

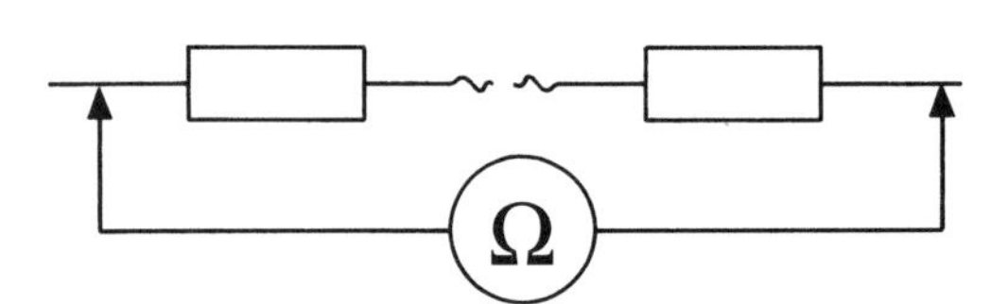

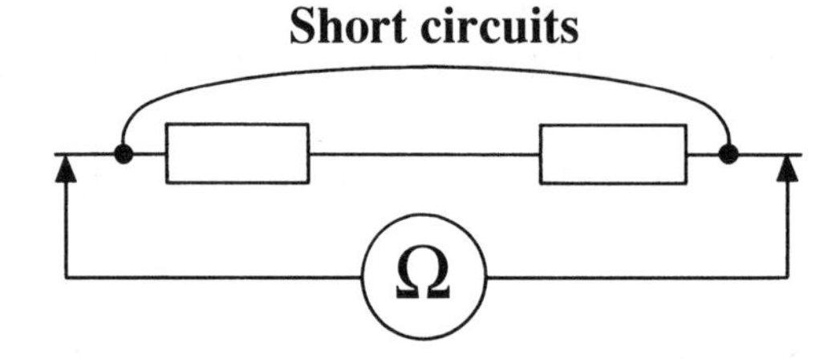

Ohmmeter reads infinite resistance

Ohmmeter reads zero resistance

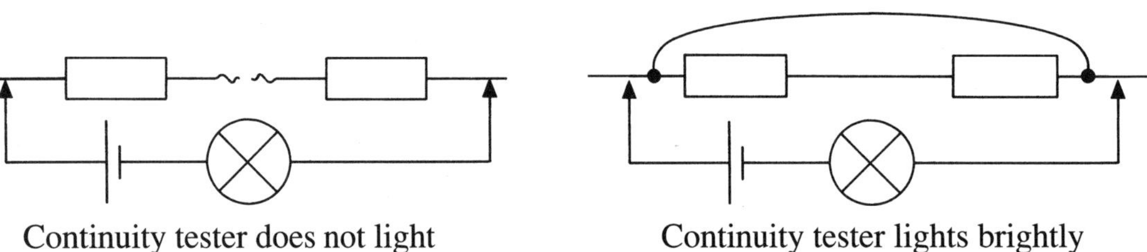

Continuity tester does not light

Continuity tester lights brightly

10. Resistors in series

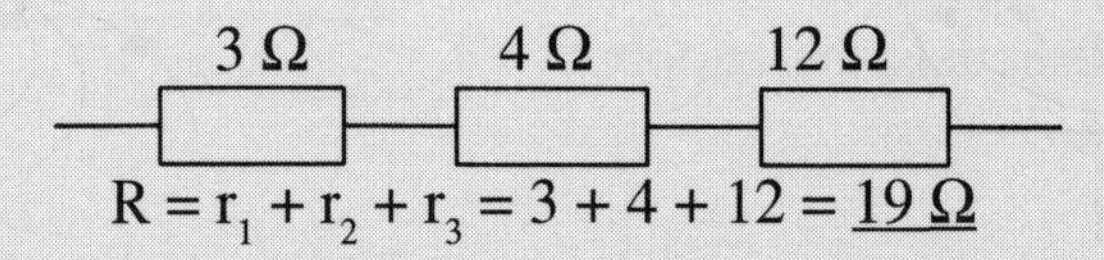

$R = r_1 + r_2 + r_3 = 3 + 4 + 12 = \underline{19\ \Omega}$

11. Resistors in parallel

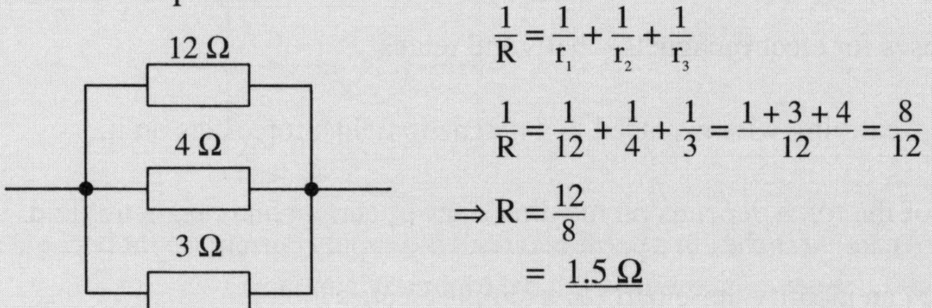

$$\frac{1}{R} = \frac{1}{r_1} + \frac{1}{r_2} + \frac{1}{r_3}$$

$$\frac{1}{R} = \frac{1}{12} + \frac{1}{4} + \frac{1}{3} = \frac{1+3+4}{12} = \frac{8}{12}$$

$$\Rightarrow R = \frac{12}{8}$$

$$= \underline{1.5\ \Omega}$$

The Mains

1. Household appliances are connected in parallel across the mains supply.

2. House wiring is protected by fuses or by circuit breakers in the consumer unit. Circuit breakers are automatic switches. They operate faster than fuses and they can easily be reset.

3. Make sure you can draw a ring main circuit.

4. Two advantages of the ring main over other parallel circuits:
   (a) The total length of cable needed is kept to a minimum.
   (b) The ring can cope with 30 A current using only 15 A cable because current can reach an appliance from 2 directions.

5. The lighting circuit is also a parallel circuit consisting of 'loops'. Thinner cable is used and there is no earth wire to the lamps.

6. When you pay your electricity bill, you pay for energy.
   Energy = Power × Time

The Mains (cont.)

7. The Electricity Companies use **kilowatt-hours**, kWh, as their units of energy. For example, a 2000 W electric fire burning for 3 hours uses $2 \times 3 = 6$ kWh of electrical energy.

8. 1 kWh = 1000 Wh = $1000 \times 60 \times 60$ Ws = 3,600,000 Joules.

Motors

1. When an electric current passes through a wire it produces a magnetic field around the wire.

A straight wire has circular field lines.

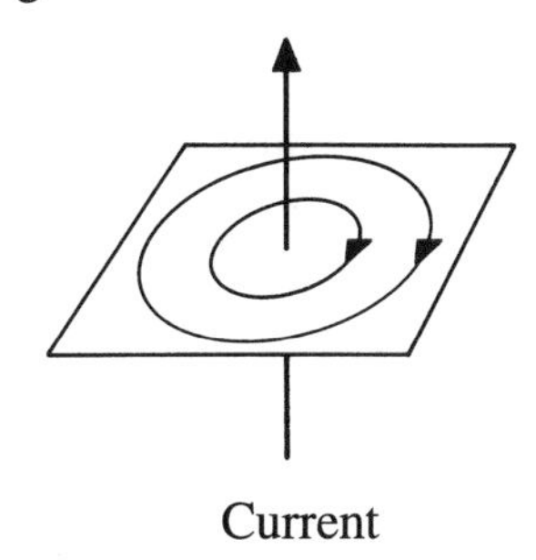

Current

A coil has a field like a bar magnet.

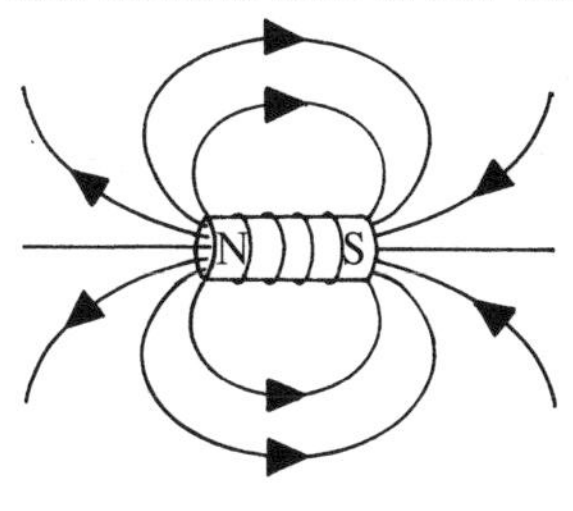

2. Look up two uses for electromagnets – bells and relays.

3. When a current-carrying wire is placed in a magnetic field a force acts on it.

4. The direction of the force depends on the directions of current and magnetic field.

5. Make sure you can identify these parts of a simple electric motor.

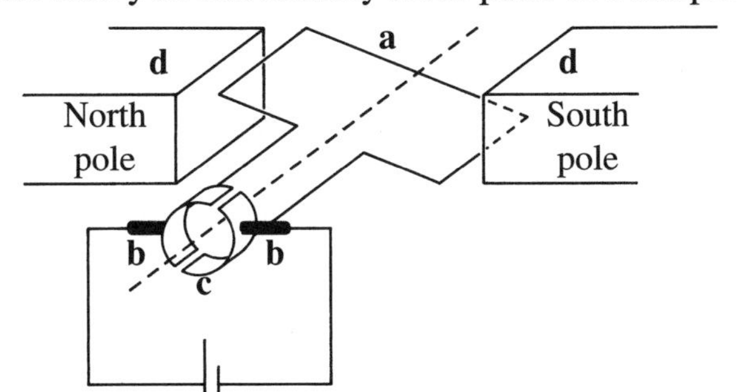

a	rotating coil (armature)
b	brushes
c	commutator
d	magnet

6. Can you explain how the motor works?

7. In commercial motors the commutators are split into many parts and there are several coils; the magnetic field is usually produced by field coils **d**.

a	rotating coil (armature)
b	brushes
c	commutator
d	field coils

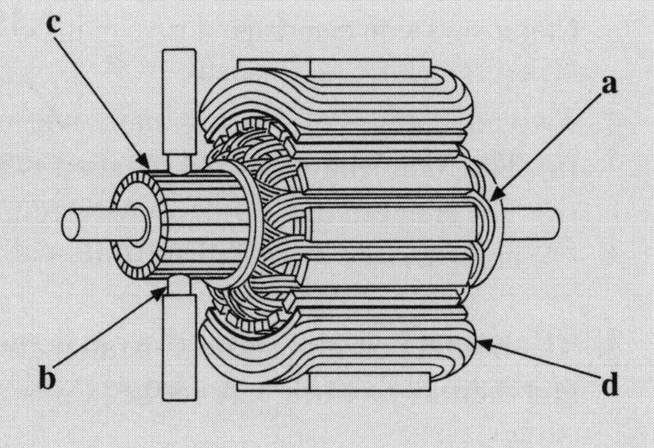

5. Health Physics

Thermometers

1. Thermometers have a physical property that changes with temperature.

2. Two examples: In a liquid-in-glass thermometer the volume of the liquid changes.
In a thermocouple the voltage changes.

3. The Clinical Thermometer

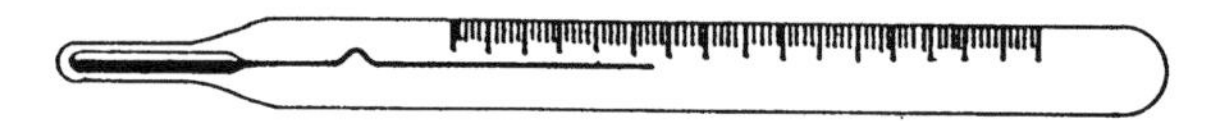

You should know:

(a) why there is a 'kink'. It's to stop the mercury falling back down the tube when the thermometer is taken out of the patient's mouth.

(b) why the glass is toughened.

(c) the tube is very narrow so that even small temperature changes will still cause the mercury column to move by a reasonable amount.

4. Normal body temperature is 37°C. If temperature rises above 40°C or falls below 35°C symptoms of illness appear.

Sound in Medicine

1. Sound travels through solids, liquids and gases but not through a vacuum.

2. The stethoscope detects sounds inside the body.

Closed bell with diaphragm for higher frequency lung sounds

Open bell touches skin for lower frequency heart sounds.

3. Humans can hear sounds in the frequency range from 20 hertz to about 20,000 hertz.

4. Frequencies above 20,000 hertz are called **ultrasonic** or **ultrasound**.

5. Ultrasound scanners are used in medicine, e.g. to produce images of unborn babies. Bursts of ultrasound can also be used to break up kidney stones. This can remove the need for surgery.

Sound in Medicine (cont.)

6. Sounds levels are measured in **decibels**, dB. Learn up a few values:

Sound	*Value in dB*
Silence	0
Conversation	60
Heavy lorry	90
Jet plane	110

7. Levels of 90 dB or more over long periods of time can cause damage to your ear.

8. Sound can also be a nuisance. What does noise pollution mean?

Refraction and the Eye

1. Refraction can cause a change in direction when light passes from air to glass or from glass to air. Learn these diagrams for the three glass shapes.

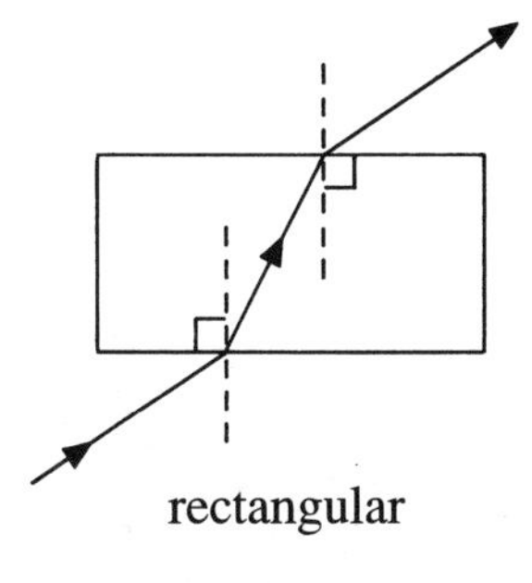

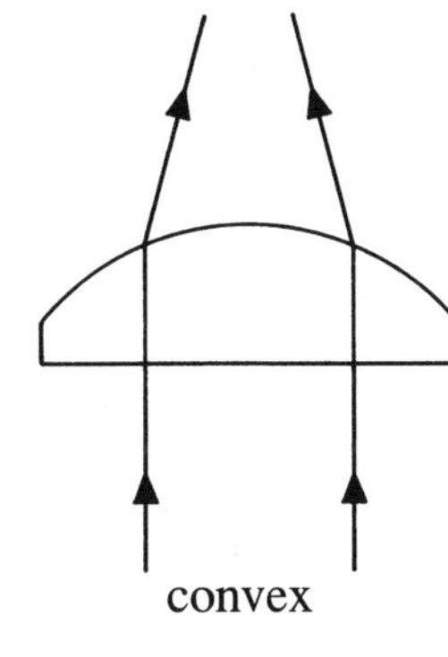

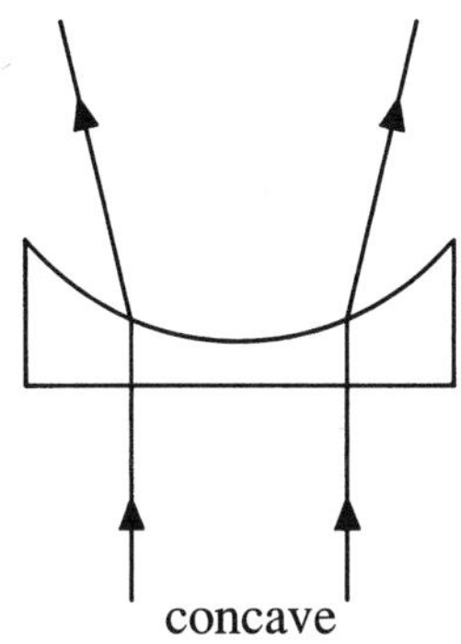

2. Copy the rectangular block diagram and write in Normal, Angle of Incidence, i, and Angle of Refraction, r.

3. The lens of the eye is a convex lens. It produces an upside down and laterally inverted (wrong way round) image on the retina.

4. Short sight

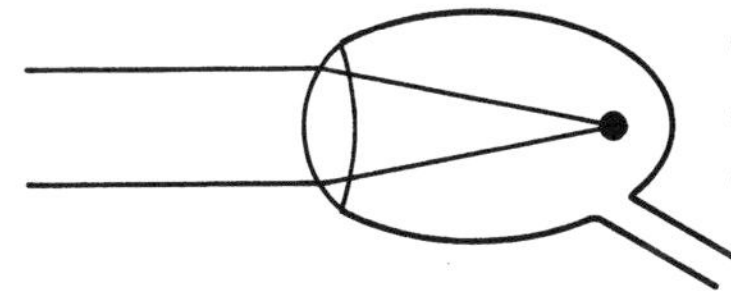

can be corrected by a **concave** lens.

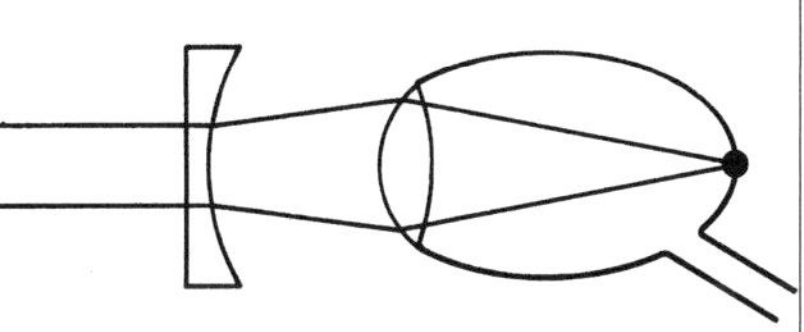

5. Long sight

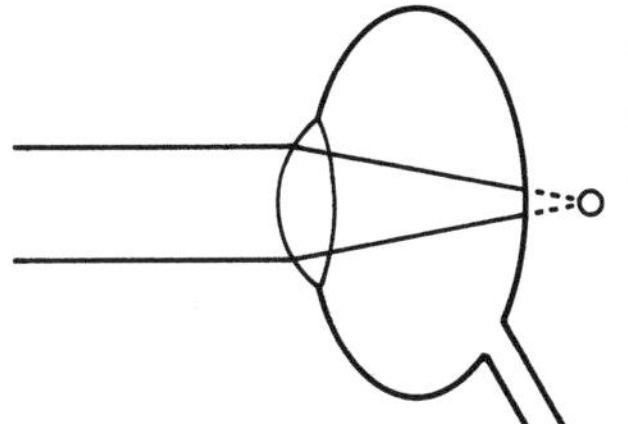

can be corrected by a **convex** lens.

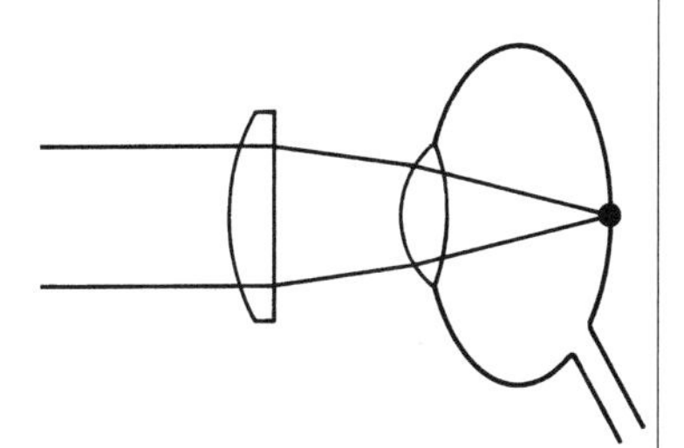

Refraction and the Eye (cont.)

6. One of the experiments you have to do is to find the focal length, f, of a convex lens. Could you describe the experiment now? You could use a lens, a piece of paper for a screen and a bright distant object.

7. Power of lens = $\dfrac{1}{\text{focal length (in metres)}}$ Power is measured in **dioptres**, D.

8. The power of a convex lens is written as a positive number; the power of a concave lens is written as a negative number, e.g. a 25 cm concave lens has a power of $-\left(\dfrac{1}{0.25}\right) = -4$ D.

9. Fibre optics make use of **total internal reflection**. Remember the diagram on page 13. Find out what an **endoscope** is. It's used to look inside you!

The Electromagnetic Spectrum

1. Lasers can provide either heat (infra red) or light to treat patients. Find out about one application of the laser in medicine, e.g. in eye surgery.

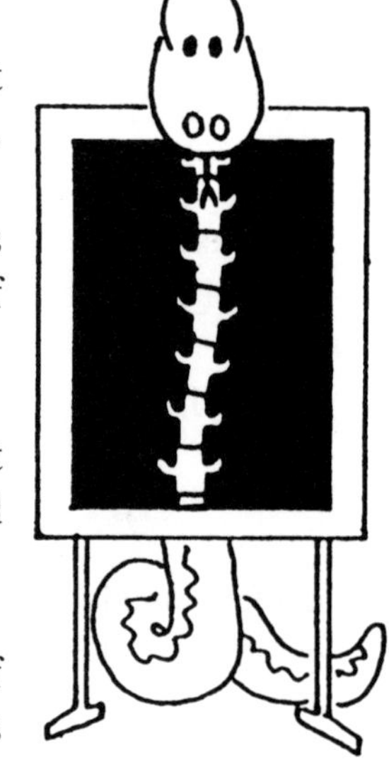

2. X-rays are very high frequency waves which pass through soft tissue but don't pass through bone. Find out about one application.

3. Computer assisted tomography (C.A.T.) uses X-rays but provides more detail than ordinary X-ray photographs with the help of computer imaging.

4. Ultraviolet (U.V.) radiation can be used to treat skin problems. It also causes a sun tan, but overexposure can damage the skin and increase the risk of skin cancers.

5. Tumours tend to give off more heat (infra red) than other parts of the body. Special cameras can be used to detect them. The photos they take are called thermograms.

6. Infra red (I.R.) radiation can be used to treat muscle strains.

Radioactivity

1. Radiation can kill living cells.

2. This is sometimes useful. Radiation can kill cancer cells or sterilise equipment by killing bacteria.

3. Radiation can easily be detected by gamma cameras, Geiger tubes, etc. Small doses can be given as 'tracers' to patients to help find tumours. Larger doses of gamma radiation can be used to destroy tumours.

Radioactivity (cont.)

4. Learn these three types of radiation:

Alpha particles	α	are Helium nuclei
Beta particles	β	are high speed electrons
Gamma rays	γ	are high frequency waves

5. Range through materials.

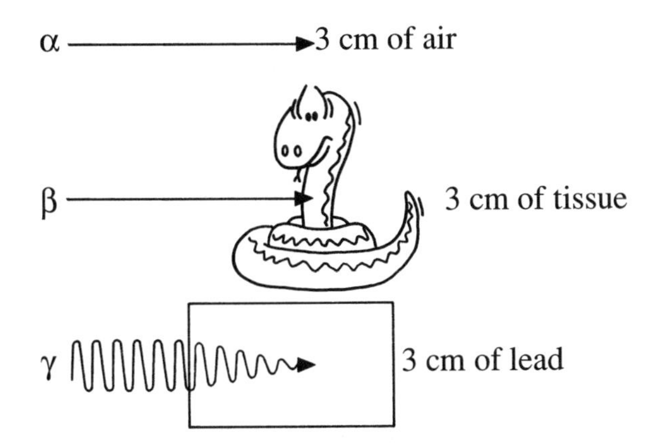

6. When a radiation is stopped by a material, it gives its energy to the material.

7. All radiation causes **ionisation**. Gamma causes a small amount, beta a little more, but alpha causes very large amounts.

8. Make sure you know what ionisation means. It happens when electrons are knocked out of their orbits by radiation.

9. And, while we are on the subject of small particles, don't forget about atoms:

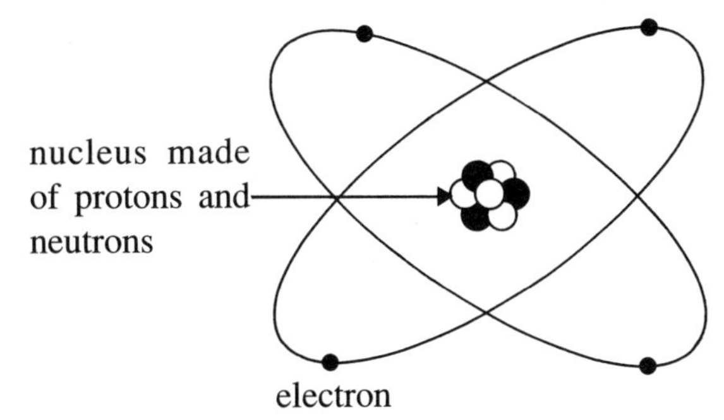

	charge (units)	*mass (units)*
electron	–1	$\frac{1}{1840}$
proton	+1	1
neutron	0	1

10. Radiation can be detected by films, Geiger tubes, etc. Check up on one method of detection.

11. The activity of a radioactive source is measured in **becquerels**, Bq. An activity of 1 Bq means one radiation comes out of the source every second.

12. Try finding the activity of a source which produces 1,380 counts in a minute. (The answer is the same as this page number!)

Radioactivity (cont.)

13. The activity of a source decreases with time.

activity
0
time

14. Half life is the time taken for the activity to reach half of its starting value.

15. You could calculate half life from a graph like this:

Time (days)	*Activity (Bq)*
0	1,000
10	250
20	62
30	15

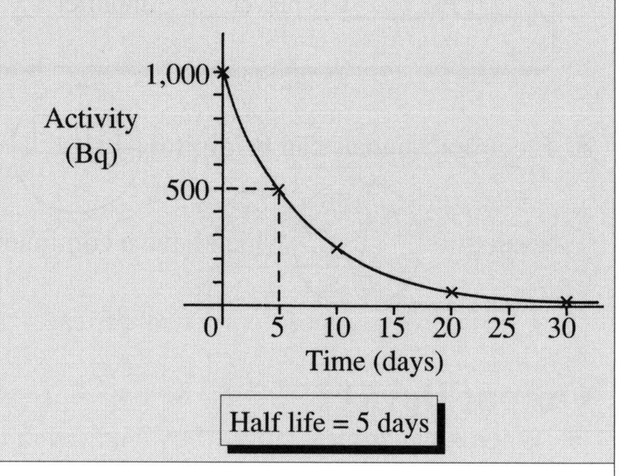

16. What safety precautions should you take when dealing with radioactive substances?

17. Dose equivalent (**dose**) is measured in **sieverts**, Sv. The sievert is the unit of radiation that applies to living things.

18. Dose equivalent gives a measure of the biological risk caused to us by radiation. It depends on the energy and the type of radiation.

6. Electronics

Basic Ideas

1. An electronic system has 3 basic parts: input, process and output.

2. Here is an example: Think of another one.

System	*Input*	*Process*	*Output*
Hi-Fi	CD player	Amplifier	Loud-speakers

3. Electronic signals can be **digital** occurring in jumps or steps, or

analogue 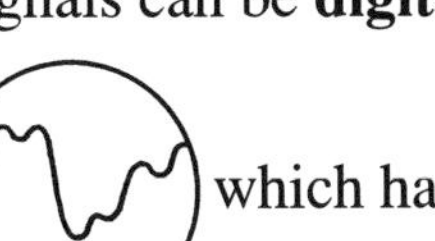 which have a continuous series of values.

Output Devices

1. Learn about two output devices, one digital and one analogue, for example:

Device	*Analogue or Digital*	*Energy Changes*
Loudspeaker	Analogue	Electrical to sound
Seven segment display	Digital	Electrical to light

2. The light emitting diode (LED) is made of two semiconductor materials. It only conducts in one direction.

Electrons flow this way only.

3. LEDs normally operate at a voltage of 2 V and take a current of around 10 mA. You often need a series resistor to protect the LED. In this circuit the full 6 volts from the battery would damage the LED. The resistor has 4 volts across it leaving 2 volts for the diode.

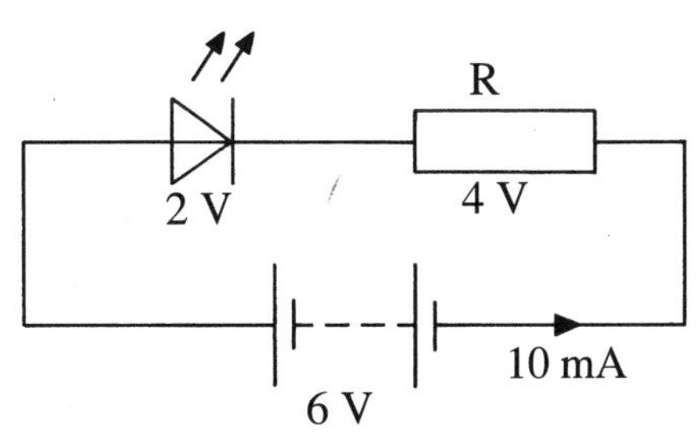

4. To calculate a value for R, use $R = \frac{V}{I}$ $\qquad V = 4\text{ V},\ I = 10\text{ mA} = 0.01\text{ A}$

$$\Rightarrow R = \frac{4}{0.01}$$

$$= \underline{400\ \Omega}$$

Output Devices (cont.)

5. The seven segment display is made of seven LEDs which can light up to form digits 0 to 9.

Copy this table and complete it up to digit 9:

Digit	*Segments lit*
0	a b c d e f
1	b c
2	a b g e d

6. Practice converting binary numbers to decimal.

2^4 *(16)*	2^3 *(8)*	2^2 *(4)*	2^1 *(2)*	2^0 *(1)*		
			1	0	= 2 + 0	= 2
		1	1	0	= 4 + 2 + 0	= 6
	1	0	0	1	= 8 + 0 + 0 + 1	= 9
1	0	0	1	0	= 16 + 0 + 0 + 2 + 0	= 18

7. Now try to convert 1101 and 11110 for yourself.

Inputs

1. A microphone changes sound energy to electrical energy. A thermocouple changes heat to electrical energy. A solar cell changes light to electrical energy.

2. A thermistor has a resistance which goes down as temperature goes up.

3. A light dependent resistor (LDR) has a resistance which goes down as the light gets brighter.

4. Use V = IR to find the resistances of the thermistors and LDRs. The first one is worked out for you.

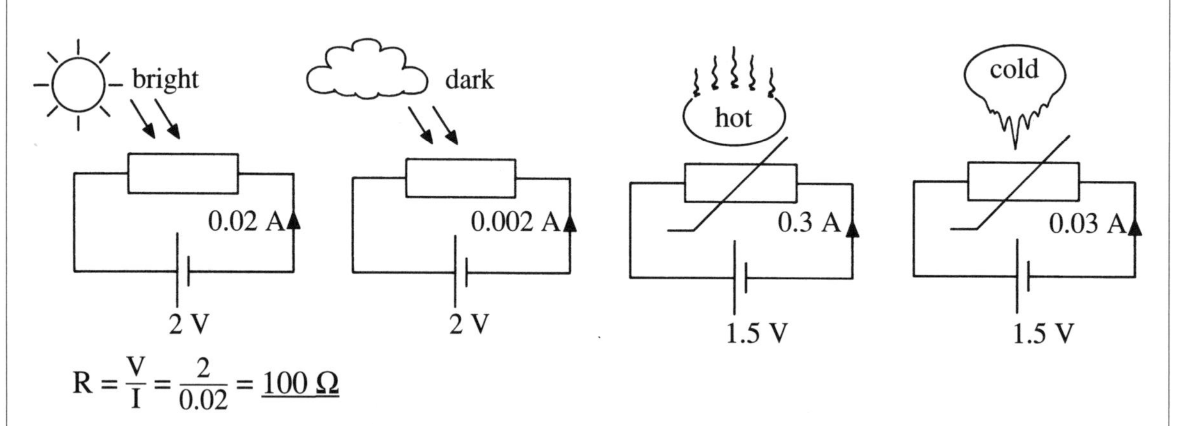

$$R = \frac{V}{I} = \frac{2}{0.02} = \underline{100\ \Omega}$$

Input Devices (cont.)

5. Make sure you know how a voltage divider works. Here are two worked examples:

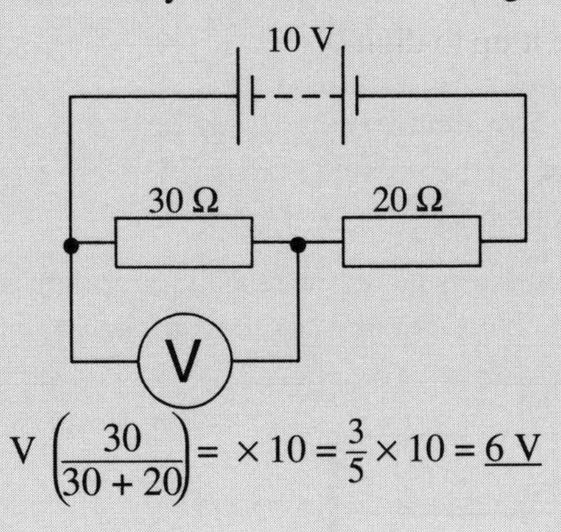

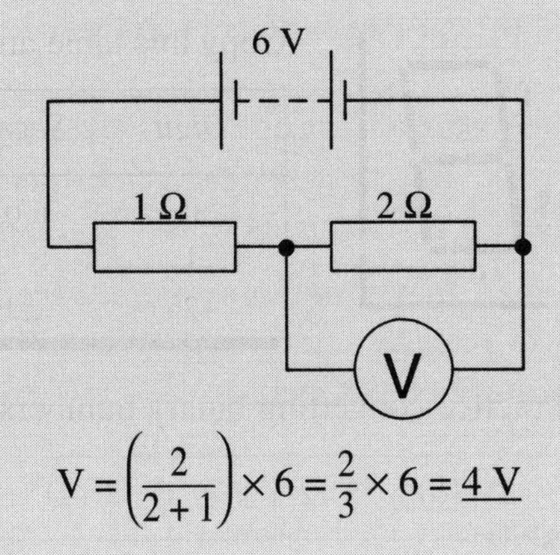

$$V\left(\frac{30}{30+20}\right) = \times 10 = \frac{3}{5} \times 10 = \underline{6\text{ V}}$$

$$V = \left(\frac{2}{2+1}\right) \times 6 = \frac{2}{3} \times 6 = \underline{4\text{ V}}$$

6. Capacitors

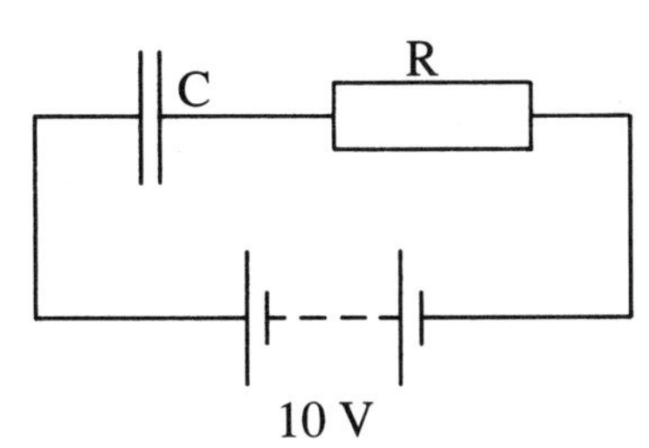

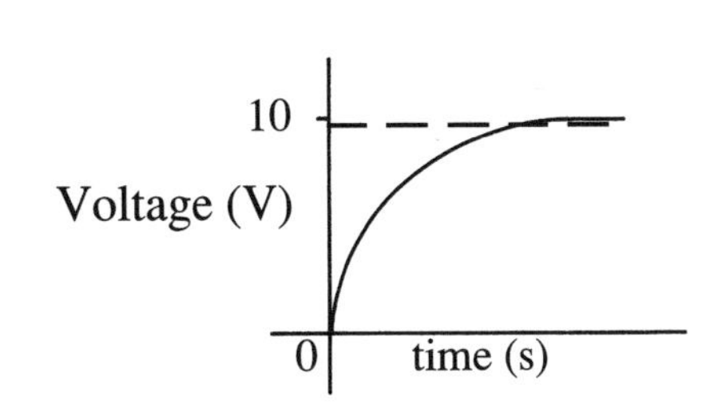

The voltage across the capacitor rises until it finally reaches the battery voltage. The capacitor is now charged up.

7. The time taken to charge the capacitor depends on C and R. The larger their values, the longer it takes to charge.

Digital Processes

1. The n p n transistor (b, c, e) can act like a switch.

2. Its three terminals are called **base**, **collector** and **emitter**.

3. Here are two practical circuits: one switches on a lamp when it becomes dark; the other lights up a warning light when a car engine overheats. Which is which?

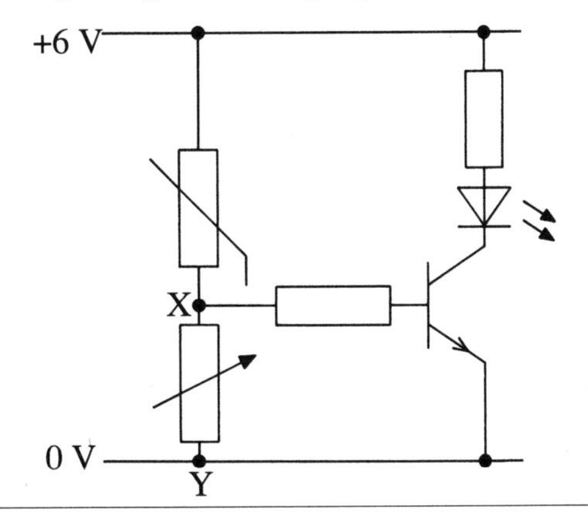

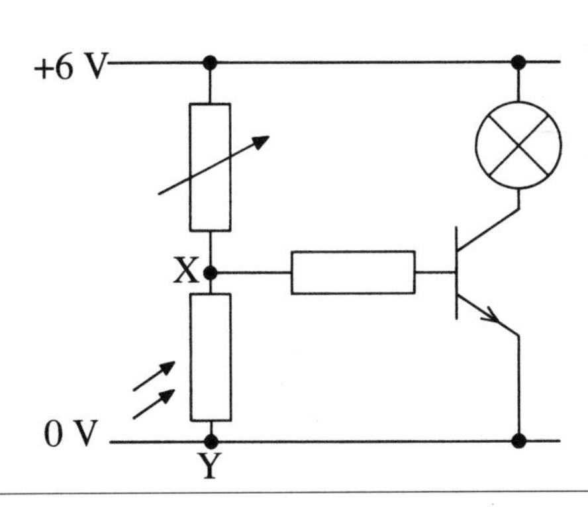

Digital Processes (cont.)

4. Try to find a **time delay** circuit using a capacitor, transistor, etc. Could you recognise all of these three circuits in an exam?

5. If you are aiming at 'genius level' try to explain how the two circuits on the previous page work. In both cases, the transistors switch on when the voltage across XY is big enough. (When that happens we say that point X has gone high.) Take it from there!

(Well, maybe one more hint – when it's hot, thermistors have low resistance and therefore low voltage across them. When it's dark, LDRs have high resistance and therefore high voltage across them.)

6.

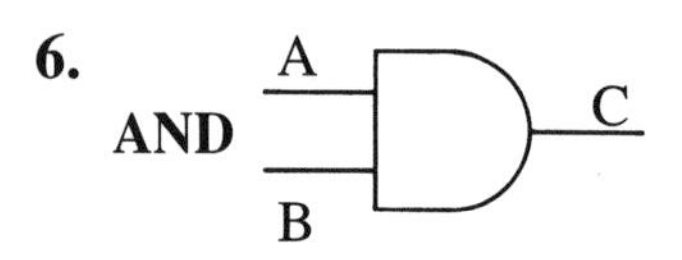

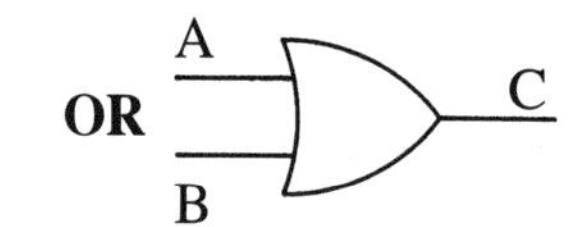

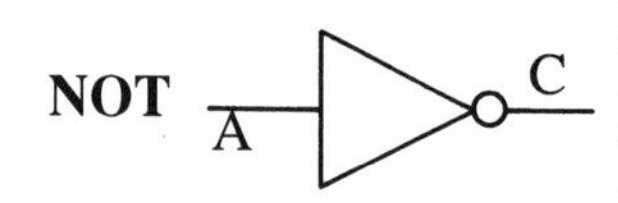

You should be able to draw and identify these three logic gates. They can be made up using transistors.

7. You should also be able to draw truth tables for each gate.

Input		*Output*
A	*B*	*C*
0	0	0
0	1	0
1	0	0
1	1	1

AND

Input		*Output*
A	*B*	*C*
0	0	0
0	1	1
1	0	1
1	1	1

OR

Input	*Output*
A	*C*
0	1
1	0

NOT

8. Remember, logic 1 = high voltage   logic 0 = low (or zero) voltage.

9. Logic circuits have many uses. Here are some:

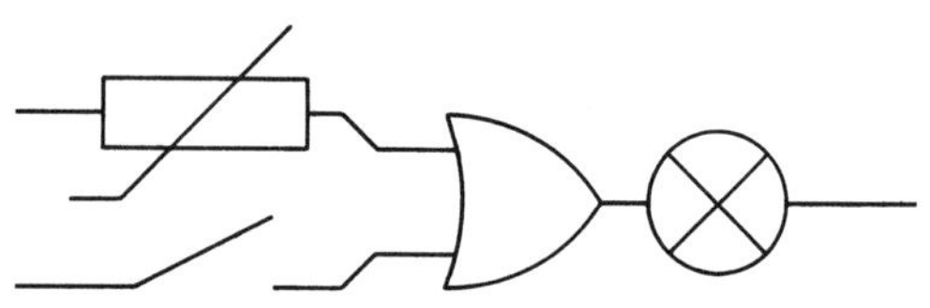

This is an overheat warning light with a switch to test whether the bulb is working. (When the thermistor is hot it produces logic 1 at the gate input.)

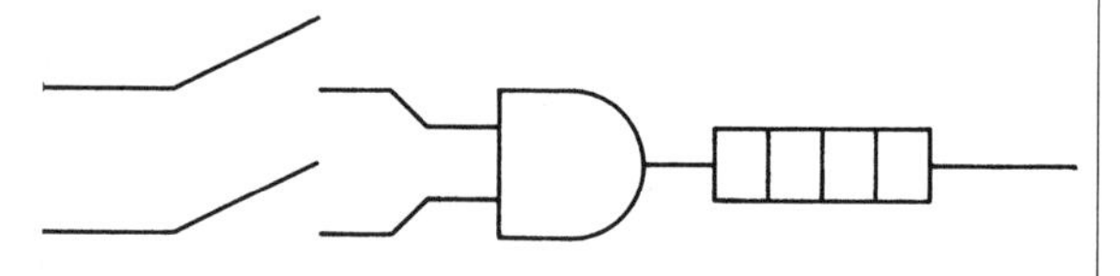

The rear heater element in a car window only operates when the heater switch is on and the car ignition switch is on.

10. The 'Prof' designed the following automatic circuit to switch on his stereo to cheer him up when his room was cold and dark. Spot the missing gate. Can you explain how it works?

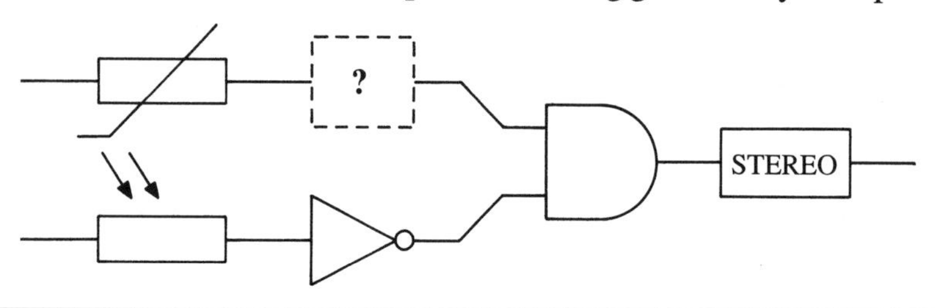

Digital Processes (cont.)

11. Practise completing truth tables where you have more than one gate.

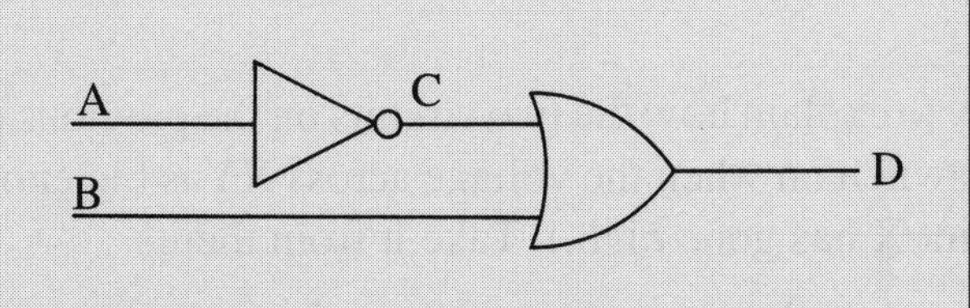

A	*B*	*C*	*D*
0	0		1
0	1	1	1
1	0	0	
1	1		

Start by putting in all the possible combinations of A and B, then go on from there and fill in the blanks.

12. Digital circuits can also be used to produce **clock pulses**. The circuits contain a **capacitor** and a **resistor** and give a **binary output**. The pulses are **counted** by special microchips. Then, with a **decoder** and a **seven segment display** you can produce a **decimal** output. A good example is a digital watch.

13. Can you explain how a clock pulse generator works? At the start of a cycle, the capacitor is uncharged – so X is low, causing Z to be high. The capacitor, C, is charged through the resistor, R, until X is high. The high input to the NOT gate causes the output, Z, to go low. This discharges the capacitor until X is low. The whole process then starts again.

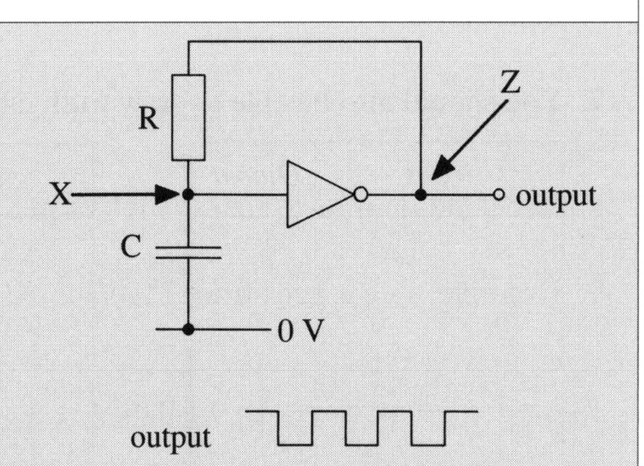

14. The clock frequency depends on R and C. The larger R, or C, the lower the frequency, i.e. the longer time between pulses.

Analogue Processes

1. Amplifiers can take a small analogue input voltage and change it into a larger analogue output voltage, as shown.

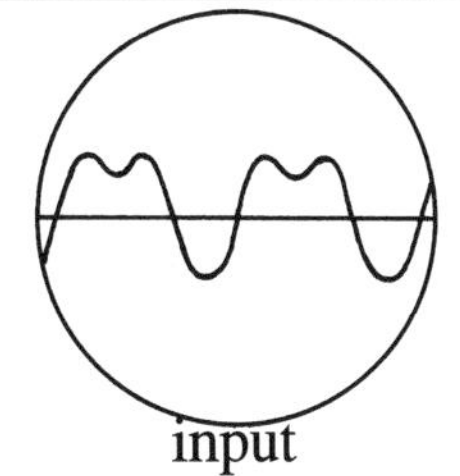

input

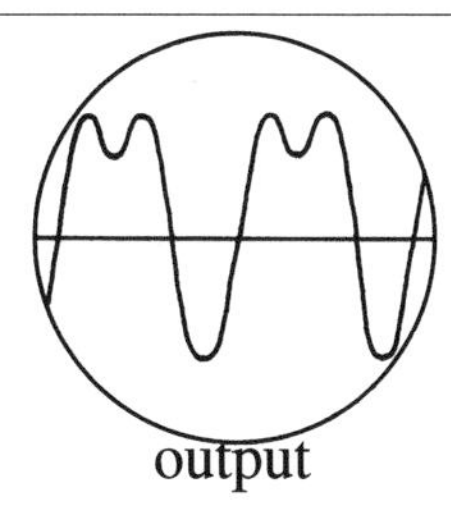

output

2. Find out about a few devices which use amplifiers, e.g. radios, hearing aids, HiFi's, intercoms. What part does the amplifier play in the device?

3. $\text{Voltage gain} = \frac{\text{Output voltage}}{\text{Input voltage}}$

4. $\text{Amplifier power} = \frac{(\text{Voltage})^2}{\text{Resistance}}$ $\quad P = \frac{V^2}{R}$

5. $\text{Power gain} = \frac{\text{Output power}}{\text{Input power}}$

7. Transport

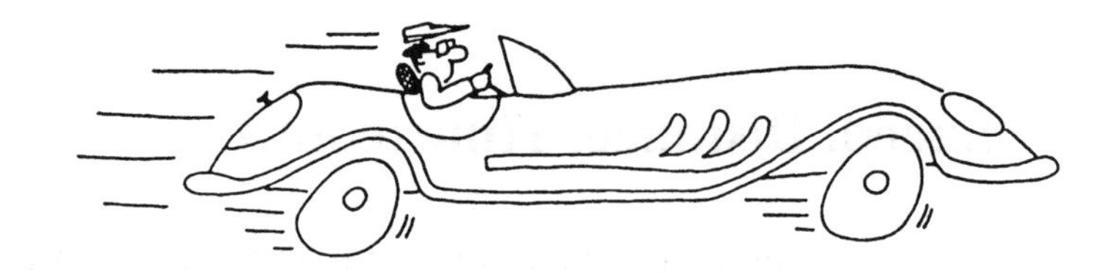

Speed, Distance, Time

1. Average speed = $\frac{\text{Distance}}{\text{Time}}$ $\quad \bar{v} = \frac{d}{t}$

2. Check up on an experiment to measure the average speed of say, a runner or a cyclist, using a stopwatch and a long measuring tape.

3. Instantaneous speeds can be calculated using the formula above. The time interval is very small. You should find out about an experiment to measure instantaneous speed. You could use a photocell and an electronic timer to measure the very small time interval.

4. Acceleration = $\frac{\text{Change of velocity}}{\text{Time}}$ $\quad a = \frac{v - u}{t}$ $\quad$ v = final velocity, u = initial velocity

5. The above equation can be changed to v = u + at. Try it!

6. Acceleration is measured in **metres per second per second**, m/s/s or m/s^2.

7. Example: A car goes from 14 m/s to 30 m/s in 10 seconds. Find its acceleration.

$$a = \frac{v-u}{t} = \frac{30-14}{10} = \frac{16}{10} = \underline{1.6\ m/s^2}$$

8. Here are some speed-time graphs:

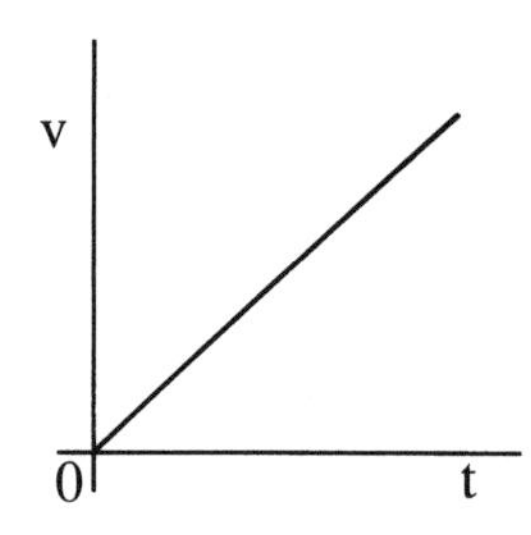

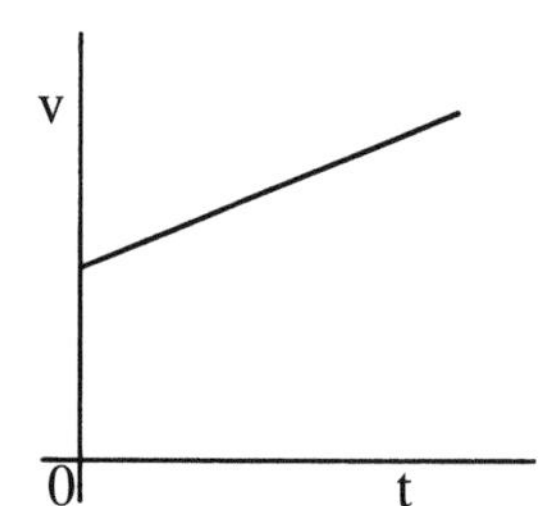

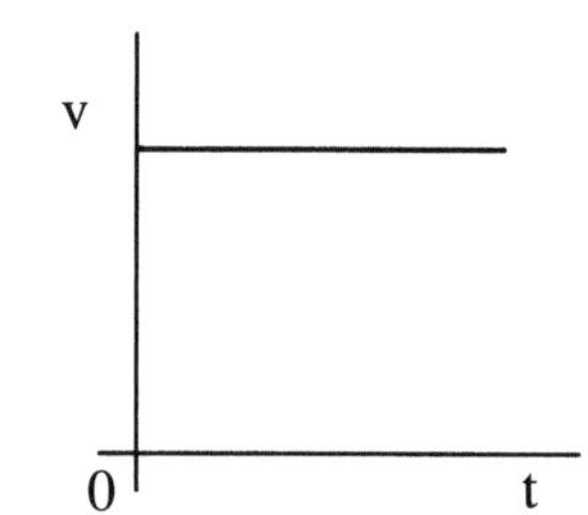

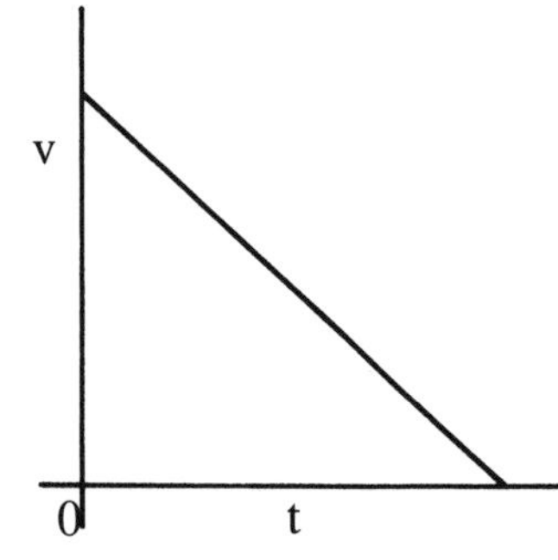

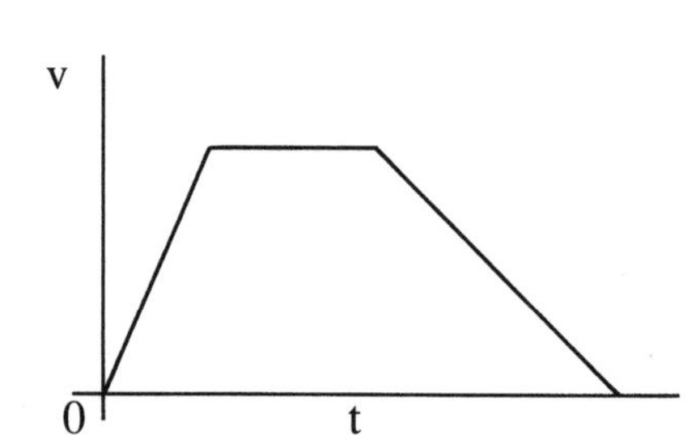

Imagine that the five graphs above describe the motion of a car on a road. Describe what is happening in each graph.

Speed, Distance, Time (cont.)

9. Acceleration can be found from a speed-time graph like this:

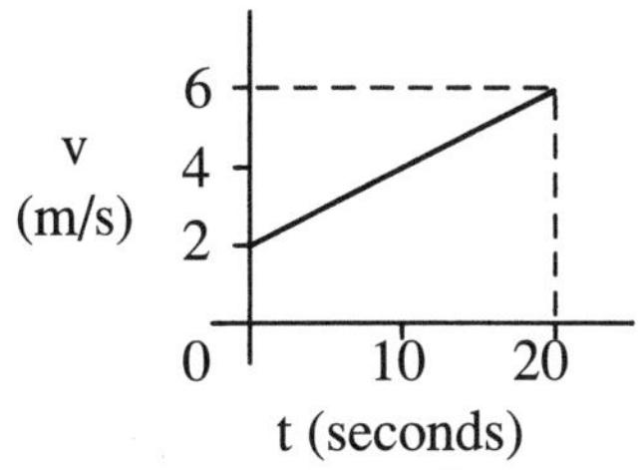

$$a = \frac{v-u}{t} = \frac{6-2}{20} = \frac{4}{20} = \frac{1}{5} = \underline{0.2\ m/s^2}$$

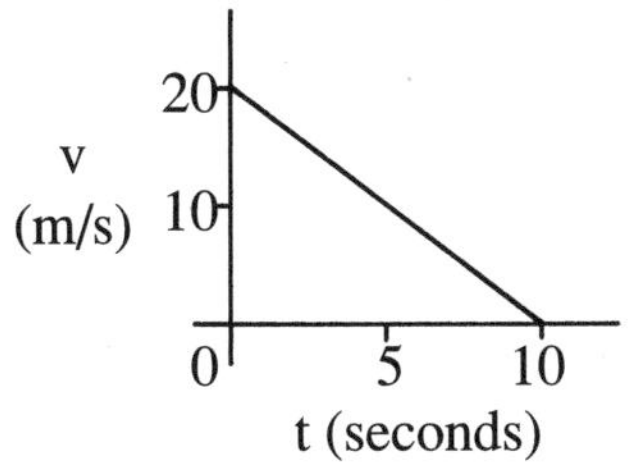

$$a = \frac{v-u}{t} = \frac{0-20}{10} = \underline{-2\ m/s^2}$$

What does the negative sign mean?

10. The distance gone can be found from the **area** under a speed-time graph:

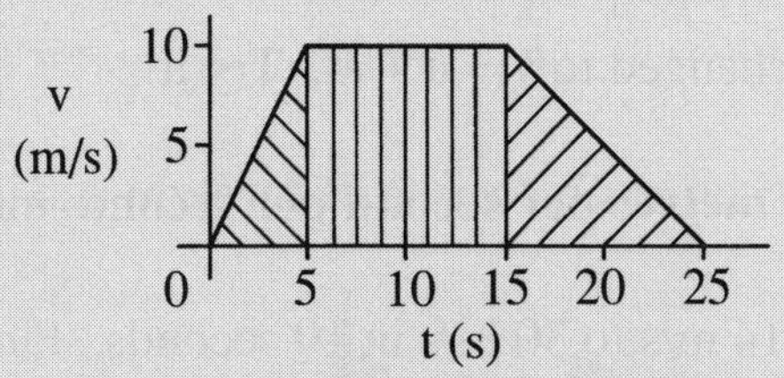

Distance = Area =

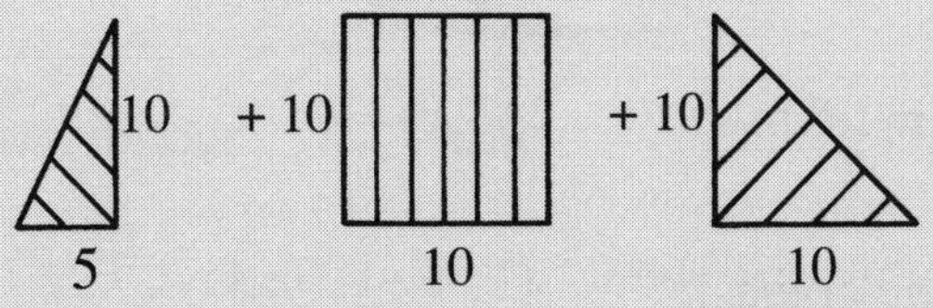

$$= \frac{1}{2}(5 \times 10) + (10 \times 10) + \frac{1}{2}(10 \times 10)$$

$$= 25 + 100 + 50 = \underline{175\ metres}$$

Forces

1. Forces can change the shape, speed, or direction of an object.

2. Force is measured in **newtons**, N. You can measure force using a spring balance – it's often called a newton balance.

3. **Newton's First Law of Motion** is a **no force** Law. It says:

   If an object is stationary or travelling in a straight line at constant speed then either there is **no force** on it or there are several **balanced forces** which cancel out.

   You could also say: 'No force means no acceleration!'

4. **Warning!** Newton's First Law can damage your health. Why is it dangerous to travel in a fast car without a seat belt? Remember, if something causes the car to stop suddenly you will tend to keep on travelling at a constant speed in a straight line!

Forces (cont.)

5. **Newton's Second Law** tells what happens when there is an **unbalanced force** acting on an object. It can be written as an equation:

Here are two examples. Their accelerations are the **same**. Find the acceleration.

6. Try this harder example. The answer is the same as in **5**.

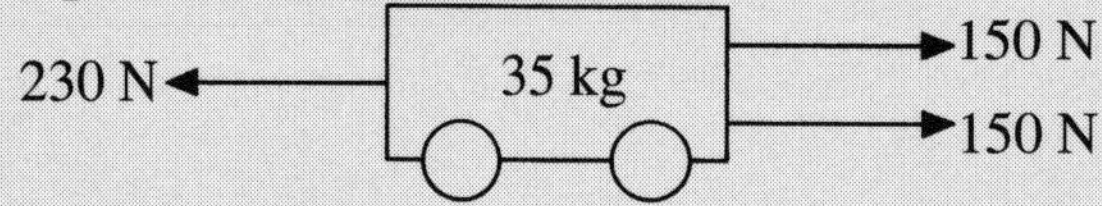

7. **Special Forces: Friction**. Check up on some real life examples of friction, where it can be helpful, e.g. brakes, and where it can be a nuisance, e.g. air resistance.

Gravity. The force of gravity on an object is called **weight** and it's measured in newtons.

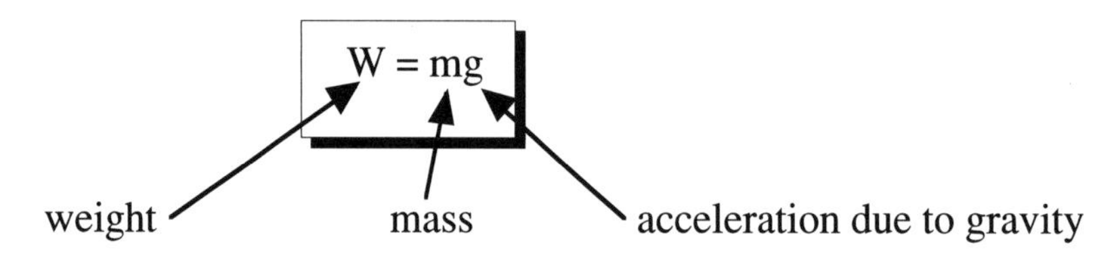

8. There is another way of thinking about 'g'. You can say:

$$g = \frac{W}{m}$$

'g' can be called Gravitational Field Strength and can be measured in newtons per kilogram, N/kg.

9. So, on Earth, $g = 10\ m/s^2$ or $g = 10\ N/kg$.

Mechanical Energy

1. When **work** is done on an object, it gains **energy**.

2. Work = Force × Distance $W = Fd$

3. Both work and energy are measured in **joules**, J.

4. When work is done to lift an object up, it gains gravitational potential energy, E_P.

$$E_P = mgh$$

5. When work is done to accelerate an object, it gains kinetic energy, E_K.

$$E_K = \frac{1}{2}mv^2$$

6. When work is done against friction, heat, E_H, is produced.

7. Here are three examples. Let's say that in each example, the Prof's 1,000 kg car has done 200,000 J of work. Let's see what happens to the work done by the car in each case.

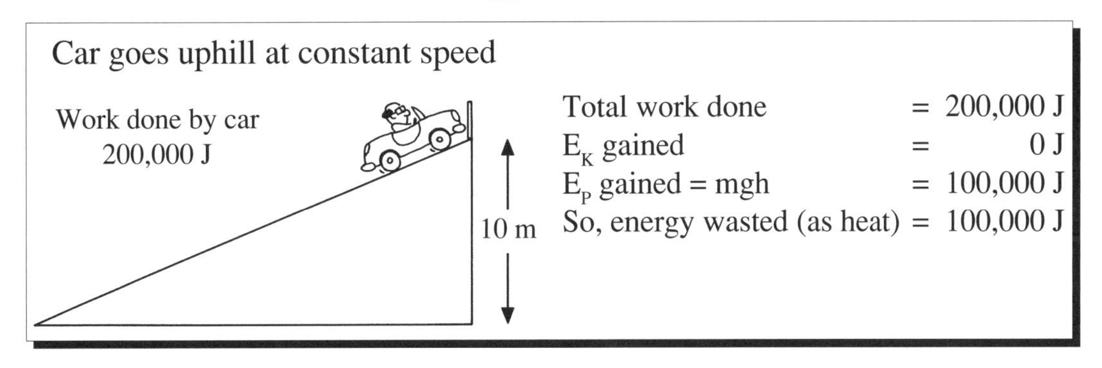

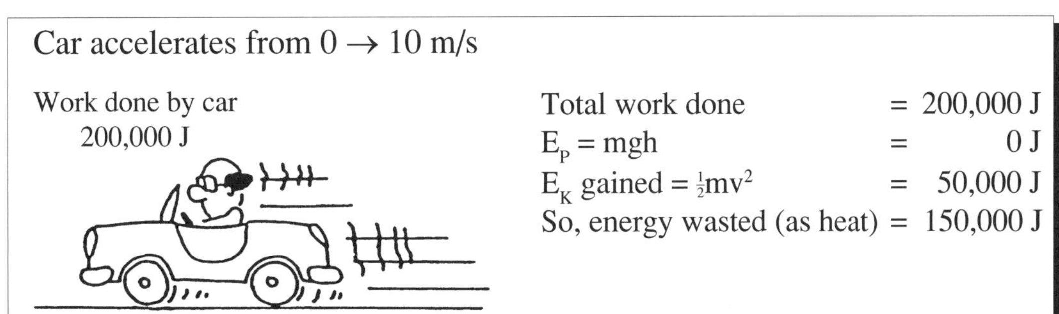

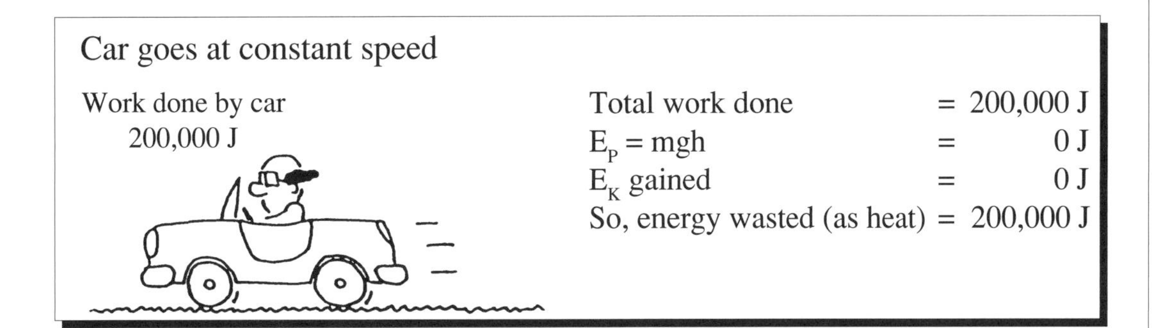

Mechanical Energy (cont.)

8. Notice that energy can change from one kind to another, but it can't disappear. Energy is **conserved**. You can't create it from nothing and you can't destroy it.

9. Power $= \frac{\text{Work}}{\text{Time}}$ or $\frac{\text{Energy}}{\text{Time}}$

$$P = \frac{E}{t}$$

10. Power is measured in **watts**, W.

11. Here are some useful power formulae:

$$P = \frac{Fd}{t} \qquad P = \frac{mgh}{t} \qquad P = Fv$$

8. Energy Matters

Energy and the Environment

1. Our main sources of energy at the moment are **fossil fuels**, e.g. oil and coal.

2. Reserves of fossil fuels are finite. What does that mean?

3. Conserving energy is important. Think of one way of conserving energy:
   (a) at home;
   (b) in industry;
   (c) in transport.

4. Can you tell the difference between renewable and non-renewable sources of energy? Here are some examples:

Renewable	*Non-renewable*
Wind energy	Coal
Solar power	Oil
Hydro power	Uranium

5. Take the three renewable sources in **4** above and explain their advantages and disadvantages.

Electricity Generation

1. Here is a block diagram showing the main stages of energy transformation in a coal fired (thermal) power station.

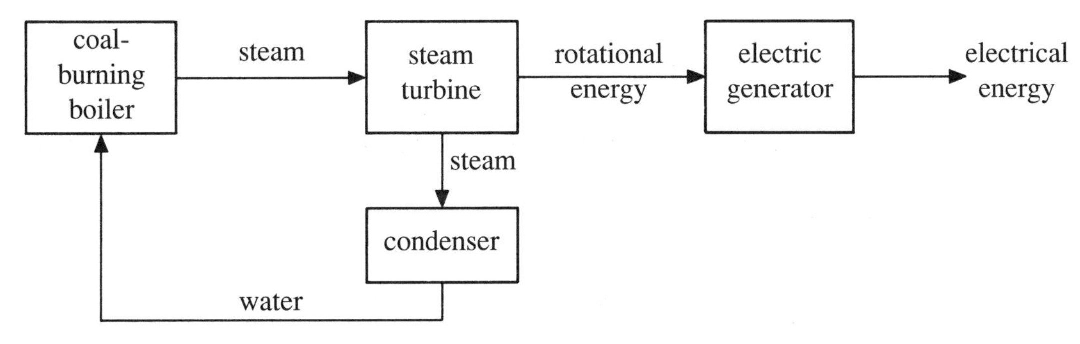

2. Draw your own block diagrams for a hydro power station and a nuclear power station.

3. Nuclear power stations produce dangerous radioactive waste.

4. Read up on a pumped hydroelectric scheme. How does it work? What are its advantages?

Electricity Generation (cont.)

5. In a hydro scheme, water falls and loses gravitational potential energy: $E_p = mgh$.

6. Look at this example of a power calculation.

Mass of water falling per second $\frac{m}{t} = 5{,}000$ kg/s

Height $h = 40$ m

Gravitational field strength $g = 10$ N/kg

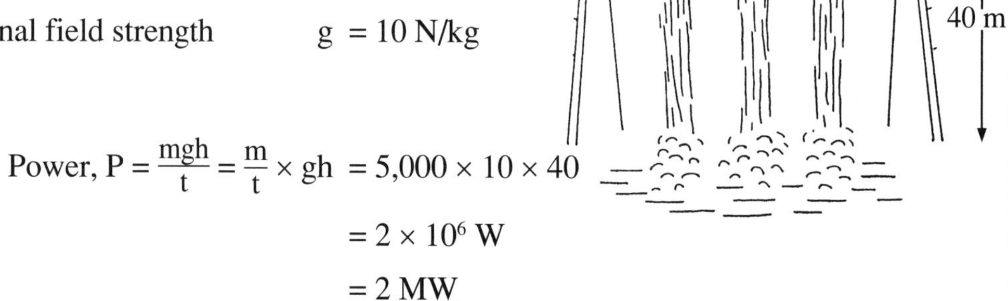

$$\text{Power, } P = \frac{mgh}{t} = \frac{m}{t} \times gh = 5{,}000 \times 10 \times 40$$

$$= 2 \times 10^6 \text{ W}$$

$$= \underline{2 \text{ MW}}$$

7. In a nuclear power station, uranium atoms break up and release neutrons in a **chain reaction**. Find a piece of paper and draw a picture of a chain reaction.

8. One gram of uranium releases about 8.2×10^{10} J. One tonne (1,000 kg) of coal releases 2.8×10^{10} J. Try to show that for equal masses of coal and uranium you get about three million times more energy from uranium. Try it now! Compare the energy released by a gram of uranium and a gram of coal!

9. $\text{Efficiency} = \dfrac{\text{Useful energy output}}{\text{energy input}}$

10. When a conductor moves through a magnetic field, a voltage can be generated.

11. The size of the induced voltage depends on the:
(a) Magnetic field strength;
(b) Number of turns of wire on the coil;
(c) Speed and direction of movement.

12. Look for a drawing of an **a.c. generator**. Can you identify the **rotor** and the **stator coils**?

13. Use the drawing to explain how the generator works. Don't just look at it. Try to explain!

14. Find out two differences between real commercial generators and the simple one you could make in class.

Electricity Transmission

1. Transformers can increase (step up) or decrease (step down) an a.c. voltage.

2. Can you identify **primary coil**, **secondary coil**, and **core** of a transformer?

3. Transformer formula: $$\frac{N_S}{N_P} = \frac{V_S}{V_P}$$

N_S means the number of turns in the secondary coil. What do the other symbols mean?

4. Transformers can never be 100% efficient because of energy losses:
(a) as heat in windings;
(b) as heat in the core; and
(c) because energy is lost in magnetising the core.

5. When electrical energy is sent long distances, power is lost due to resistance of the power lines.

6. Using high voltages reduces power loss because this allows smaller currents in the power lines.

7. Power loss = I^2R. Look at the following example and try to understand all the numbers!

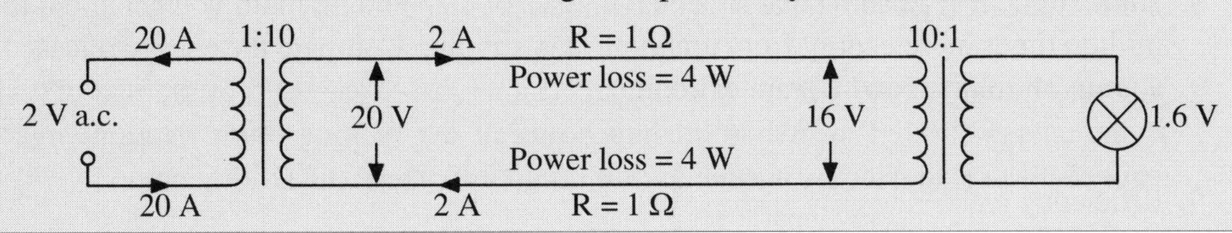

8. And finally – what's the **national grid**? Find out some details.

Heat in the Home

1. First of all, some names. **Temperature** means how hot or cold something is. It's measured in **degrees Celsius**. **Heat**, E_H, is a form of energy. Remember, energy is measured in **joules**.

2. Heat can travel in three ways:

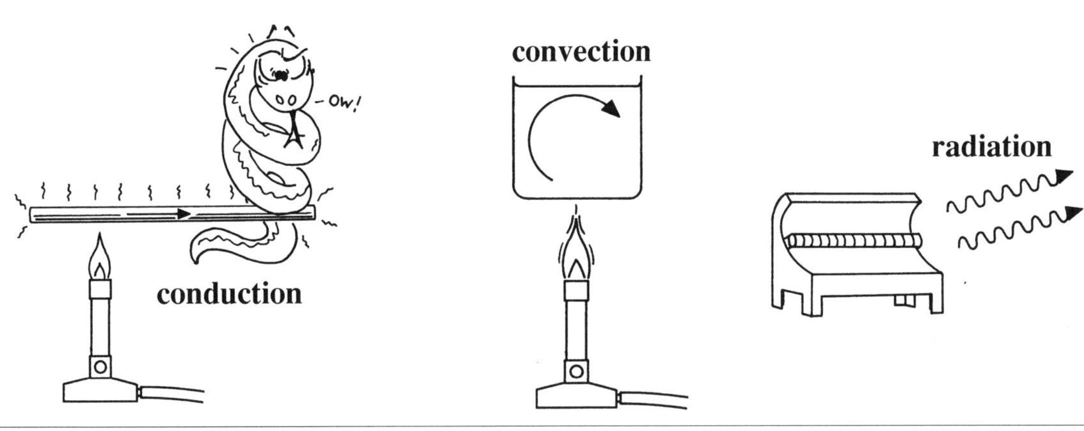

Heat in the Home (cont.)

3. Your home loses heat due to conduction, convection and radiation. You can reduce heat loss in several ways.
   (a) The air trapped between the two panes of a double-glazed window reduces heat loss by conduction.
   (b) Cavity wall insulation can reduce heat loss by convection.
   (c) Metal foil can reduce heat loss by radiation.

4. The heat lost every second depends on the temperature difference, ΔT, between the inside and outside of your house. The greater ΔT, the greater the heat loss.

5. The heat required to raise the temperature of 1 kg of material by one degree is called **specific heat capacity**, c.

$$c = \frac{E_H}{m\Delta T}$$

$$E_H = cm\Delta T$$

6. Specific heat capacity is measured in **joules per kilogram degree Celsius**, J/kg°C.

7. Heat can come from several sources:

Electrical $E_H = ItV$

Mechanical $E_H = Fd$ $E_H = mgh$ $E_H = \frac{1}{2}mv^2$

8. Solid, liquid and gas are three states of matter.

9. When a **change of state** occurs, **latent heat** is either lost or gained. **Latent heat of fusion** is the energy needed to melt solid into liquid at the melting point. **Latent heat of vaporisation** is the energy needed to boil liquid into gas at the boiling point.

10. While a change of state is occurring in the substance, its temperature stays constant.

11. Specific latent heat, L, is the energy required to change the state of 1 kg of a material.

$$L = \frac{E_H}{m}$$

$$E_H = mL$$

12. Latent heat is measured in **joules per kilogram**, J/kg.

9. Space Physics

Signals from Space

1. You should know the meanings of the following:

   universe, **galaxy**, **star**, **sun**, **solar system**, **planet**, **moon**.

   Try writing a few sentences to include all these terms starting:

   'Our universe is made up of millions of galaxies. The galaxies contain stars......'

2. The **distance** travelled by light in one year is a **light year**. Smaller distances can be measured in light minutes or light seconds.
   A light year = $3 \times 10^8 \times 60 \times 60 \times 24 \times 365$ metres.
   Try working out this distance using a calculator.

3. Learn these three distances:

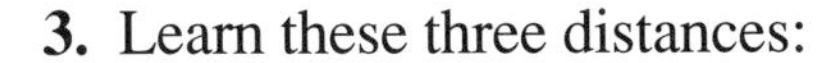

From Earth to the sun	500 light seconds
To next nearest star	4.3 light years
Across the galaxy	100,000 light years

4. The Astronomical Telescope.

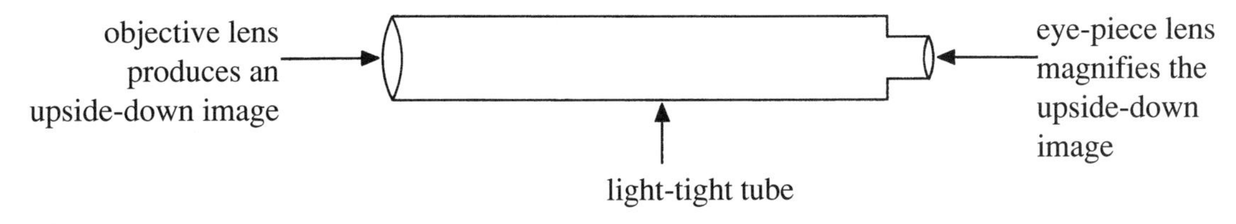

5. The brightness of the image depends on the diameter of the objective lens. The larger the objective lens, the more light hits it and so the brighter the image is.

6. The magnifying glass.

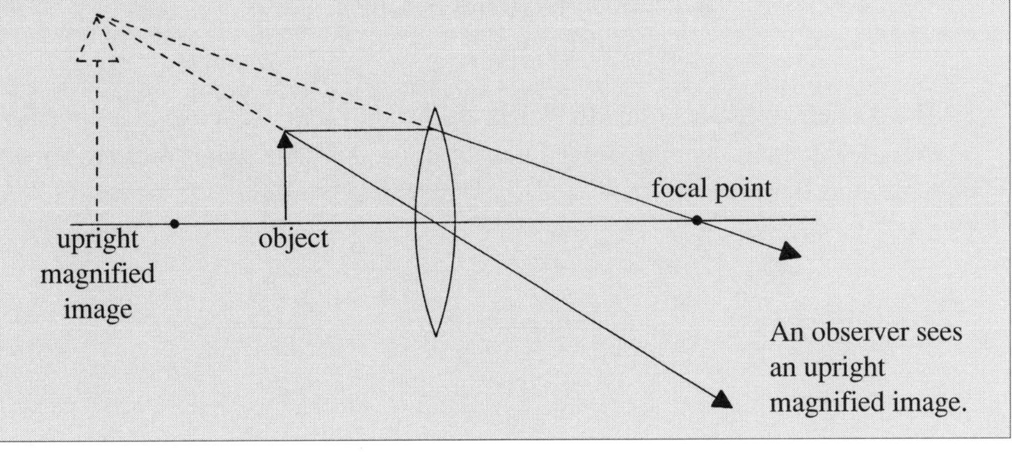

Signals from Space (cont.)

7.

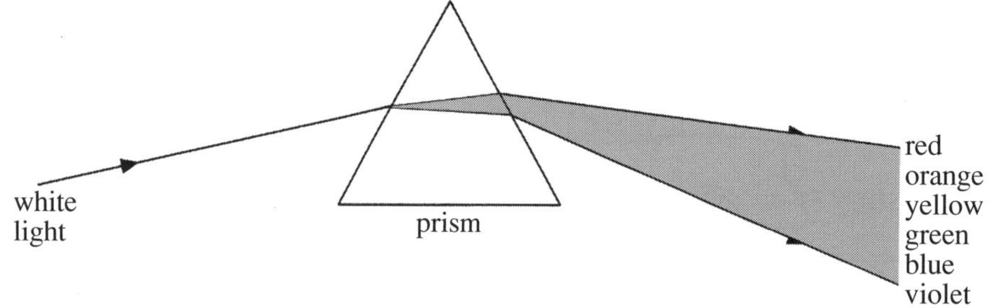

White light is a mixture of colours (frequencies). The glass prism splits up the light to make a continuous spectrum.

8. Gases like sodium vapour and mercury vapour in discharge tubes can produce a line spectrum. The different lines tell which atoms are present in the gas. This can be useful when looking at the light from stars to see what elements they are made of.

9. The electromagnetic spectrum contains waves of a wide range of wavelengths. They all travel through space at 3×10^8 m/s.

10. Longest λ, Lowest f → Shortest λ, Highest f

Name of waves	Radio	TV	Micro-waves	Infra red	Visible	Ultraviolet	X-rays	Gamma rays
Detector	radio or TV receiver		microwave diode	ther-mometer	eye or film	fluorescent ink	photo-graphic plate	Geiger counter

11. Do all telescopes have glass lenses? Check up on some details of **radio telescopes**.

Space Travel

1. The rocket in space

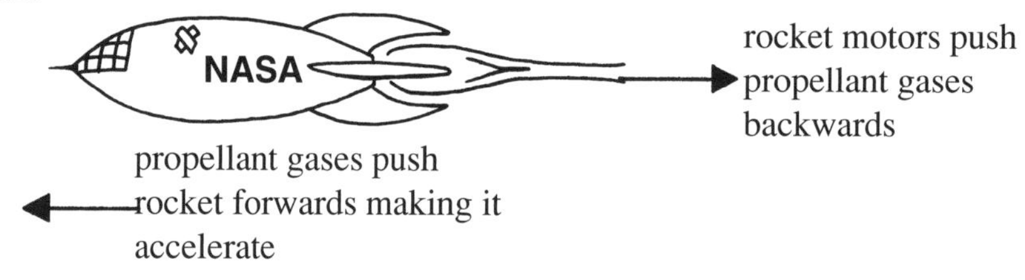

2. The rocket works according to **Newton's Third Law**. 'If A exerts a force forwards on B, then B will exert an equal force backwards on A.' The two forces are sometimes called a Newton Pair.

Space Travel (cont.)

3. Here is another example of a Newton Pair:

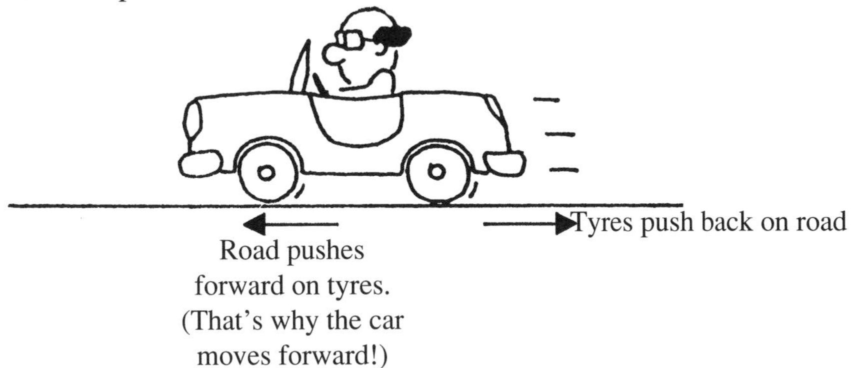

4. Remember

Go back and take a look at paragraphs **5** to **9** in **Forces** in the **Transport** chapter.

5. Now work out the accelerations of the rockets and show that they are all the same:

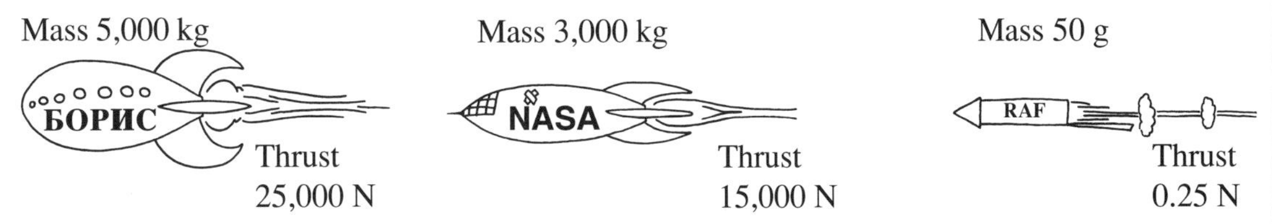

6. Once a rocket has accelerated up to its 'cruising speed' in space, its engines can be switched off. The rocket will keep going at constant speed in a straight line. Remember Newton's First Law on page 31? Check it!

7. Experiments show that all objects have the same acceleration near the surface of the Earth (if air resistance is very small).

8. The value of the acceleration due to gravity, 'g', is different on different planets. The mass of an object doesn't change but its weight does.

On Earth, g = 10 m/s^2 or 10 N/kg

On Jupiter, g = 26 m/s^2 or 26 N/kg

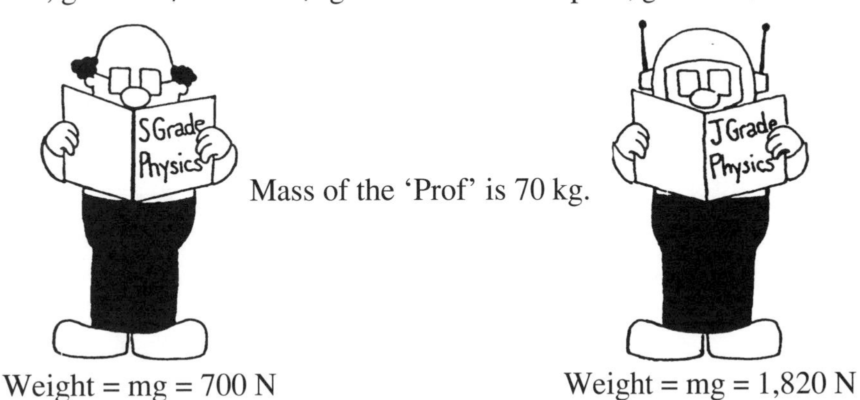

Space Travel (cont.)

9. Notice that the 'Prof' has a weight of 700 N on the **surface** of the Earth. As he moves away from the planet, 'g' decreases and so his weight will decrease. Finally, if he ever got completely out in space away from all the gravitational fields, he would be weightless.

10. Objects can appear to be weightless even near the surface of the Earth – that happens when they are in free fall.

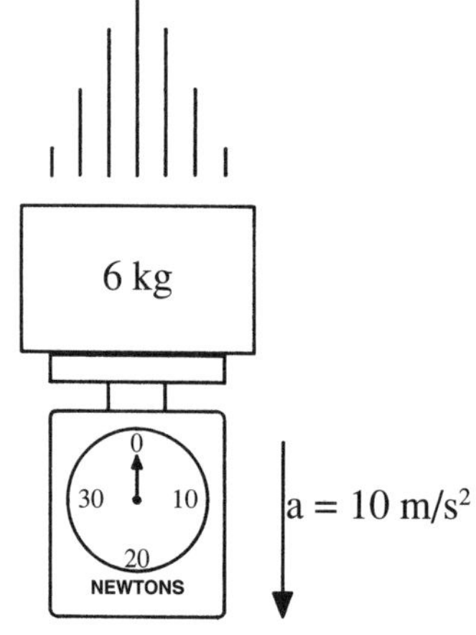

11. If an object is fired horizontally, the force of gravity pulls it down. It has a path called a **parabola** which is the combined effect of a horizontal motion and a vertical motion.

12. The projectile motion is a combination of:

(a) constant horizontal velocity

(b) uniform acceleration vertically.

Look at the diagram below; it shows the horizontal (v_H) and vertical (v_V) velocities of a projectile launched at a horizontal velocity of 10 m/s:

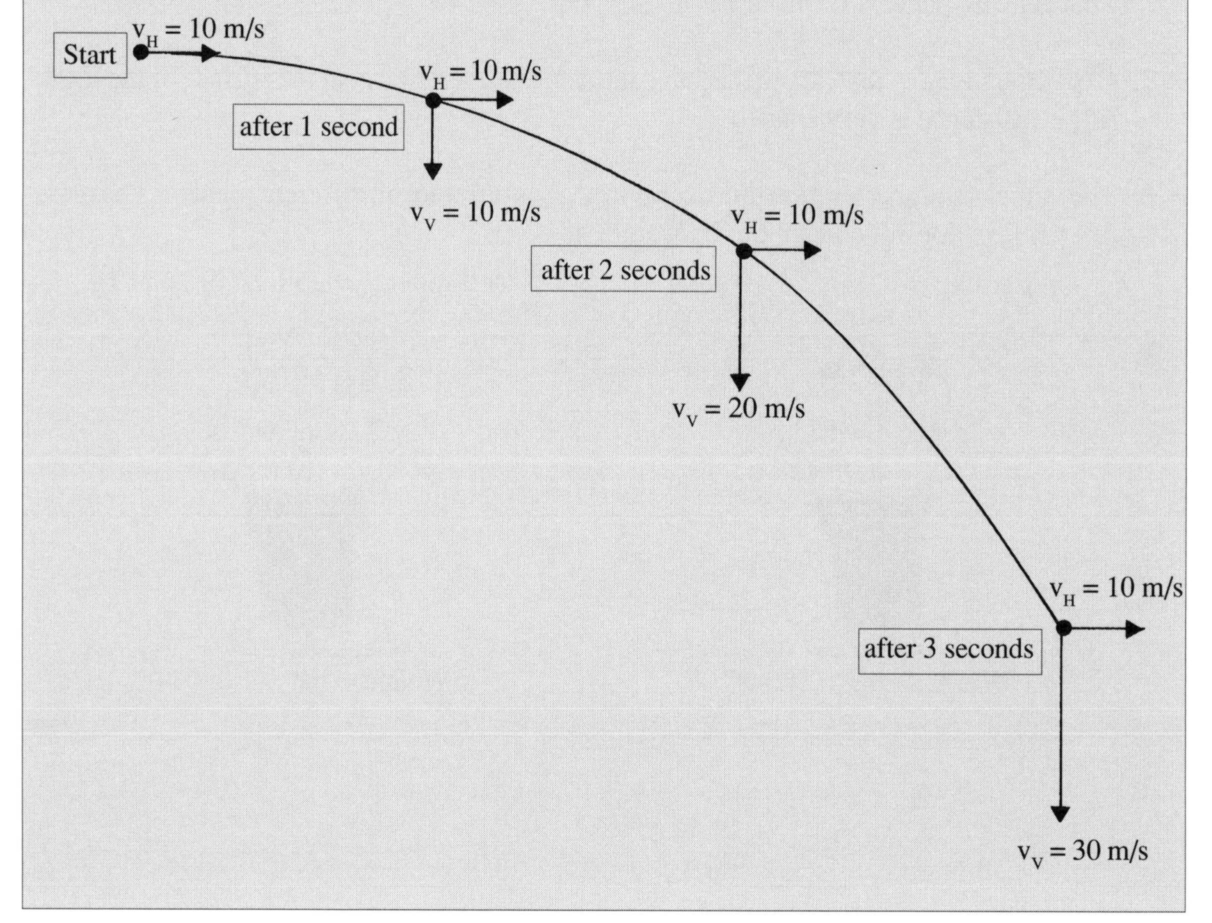

Space Travel (cont.)

13. Do you know that satellite motion is a type of projectile motion and that satellites 'fall' towards the Earth in orbit? Look up Newton's Thought Experiment.

14. Look out for questions on space vehicles heating up on re-entry from space. The air in the atmosphere causes friction. This reduces kinetic energy. The lost kinetic energy becomes heat.

15. Try to show that when a 2,000 kg spacecraft re-enters the atmosphere and slows from 2,000 m/s to 1,000 m/s then 3×10^9 J of heat is produced.

16. Make sure you know the formulae:

$E_H = cm\Delta T$ $W = Fd$ $E_K = \frac{1}{2}mv^2$

When kinetic energy changes to heat:

$$\frac{1}{2} \not{m} v^2 = c \not{m} \Delta T$$

When friction forces cause heat:

$$F d = c m \Delta T$$

10. Practice Questions

Try the following practice questions. They are very similar to the kind you will meet in the examination. Some outline answers are available on page 48.

General level

1. Which entry below gives the declared voltage and the frequency of the mains electrical supply in your home?

	Voltage (volts)	*Frequency (hertz)*
A	110	60
B	110	0
C	230	100
D	230	60
E	230	50

2. The energy change taking place at the mouthpiece of a telephone is

A chemical to sound
B sound to chemical
C chemical to electrical
D sound to electrical
E electrical to sound.

3. The pictures seen on a colour television screen are produced by mixing the following colours of light:

A	red	yellow	green
B	red	yellow	blue
C	red	green	blue
D	green	yellow	blue
E	red	blue	violet.

4. Your household electrical appliances are connected in parallel so that they have the same

A fuse rating
B voltage applied
C resistance
D flex rating
E current supplied.

5. The nucleus of an atom contains

A protons and neutrons
B neutrons only
C neutrons and electrons
D protons and electrons
E electrons only.

General level (cont.)

6. Which of the following is the circuit symbol for a NOT gate?

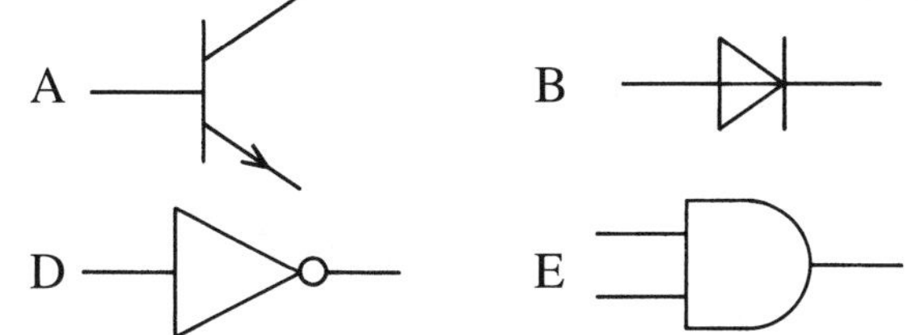

7. During a test drive, a car goes from 0 to 40 miles per hour in 10 seconds. Which of the following gives the acceleration of the car in miles per hour per second?

A 0.2
B 5
C 4
D 48
E 400

8. The graph shows the speed of a runner during the first 3 seconds of a race.

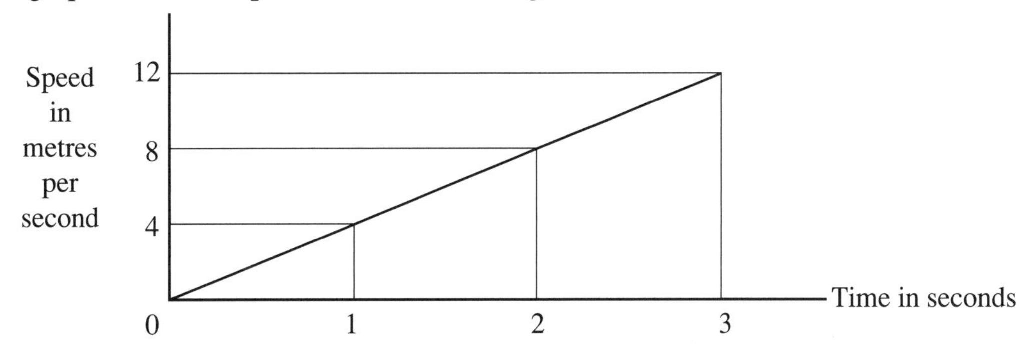

The runner's acceleration, in metres per second per second, is

A 0.25
B 4
C 6
D 18
E 36

9. The energy needed to change a solid to a liquid, without a change in temperature, is called

A the latent heat of vaporisation
B the freezing point
C the specific heat capacity
D the melting point
E the latent heat of fusion.

10. The diagrams show the temperatures inside and outside the same house on different days. In which case is the heat loss from the house, in a given time, greatest?

A 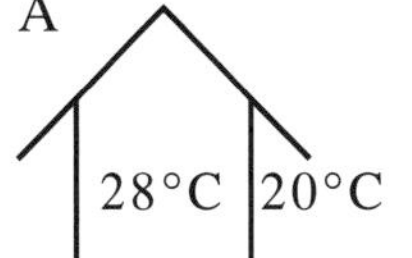

B 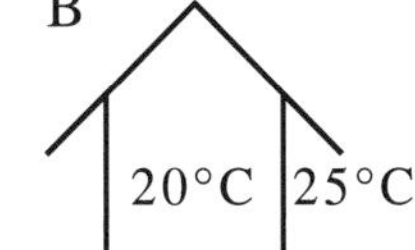

C 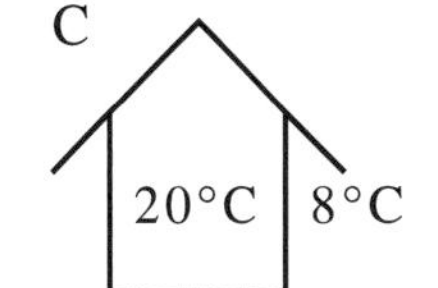

D 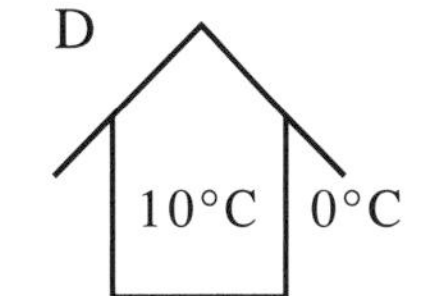

E 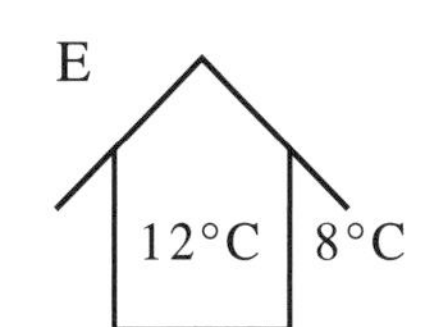

General level (cont.)

11. The diagram shows a ray of light X striking a plane mirror. Which path shows the reflected ray?

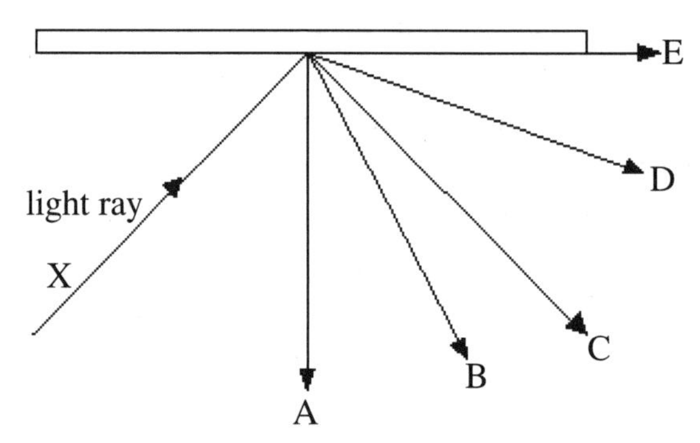

12. A galaxy is a group of

A stars
B satellites
C moons
D planets
E chocolate bars.

Credit level

1. A girl has a pair of spectacles with lenses of power +1.5 D.

(a) Calculate their focal length.
(b) Is she long sighted or short sighted?
(c) Describe an experiment she could carry out to check the focal length of one of the lenses.

2. (a) What is meant by *gravitational field strength*?
(b) Complete the last two columns of the table below to show an astronaut's mass and weight in different situations.

Situation	*Gravitational field strength*	*Mass*	*Weight*
On the Earth	10 N/kg	70 kg	
In deep space	negligible		
On the Moon	1.6 N/kg		

3. The distance from Earth to the nearest star, Proxima Centauri, is 4.3 light years. **Estimate** the month and year in which light radiated on 1st Jan 1995 from Proxima Centauri would be seen on Earth.

Credit level (cont.)

4. (a) What is meant by ultrasound?

(b) Ultrasonic waves have a frequency of 8.0 MHz. They travel through human tissue at 1,600 m/s.
Calculate the wavelength of the ultrasound in human tissue.

(c) A range of different ultrasonic frequencies can be used in medicine. Shorter wavelengths of ultrasound allow sharper images to be produced.
Why does a probe of 8.0 MHz frequency give a sharper image than one of 2.25 MHz?

(d) Give **one** example of the use of ultrasound in medicine.

(e) Why is ultrasound safer than X-rays for some medical investigations?

5. The NASA space shuttle has a mass of 68,500 kg. After re-entry, it has a touchdown speed of 93.0 m/s and travels 2.00 km along the runway before stopping.

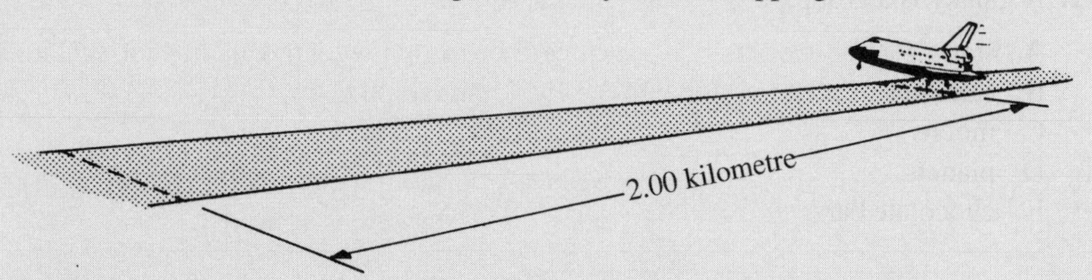

(a) Calculate the kinetic energy of the shuttle at the instant of touchdown.

(b) What is the size of the force necessary to stop the shuttle in the 2.00 kilometre distance?

(c) During re-entry, the orbital speed of 7,800 m/s is reduced to the touchdown speed of 93 m/s. The shuttle experiences a large reduction in its kinetic energy when this happens.
Explain what happens to this 'lost' kinetic energy.

(d) The aluminium alloy body of the shuttle is covered with a layer of tiles made from silica.
Suggest one property of the silica tiles which would be of use during the re-entry of the shuttle. Explain your answer.

Answers

General level

1. E
2. D
3. C
4. B
5. A
6. D
7. C
8. B
9. E
10. C
11. C
12. A

Credit level

1. (a) focal length = $\frac{1}{1.5}$ = 0.67 m = 67 cm

(b) long sighted (The plus sign indicates a convex lens which is used to correct long sight.)

(c) See page 22, 'Refraction and the Eye', paragraph **6**.

2. (a) Gravitational field strength = $\frac{\text{weight}}{\text{mass}}$ or the force of gravity acting upon each kilogram of mass.

(b)

Mass (kg)	*Weight (N)*
70	700
70	0
70	112

3. 4.3 years ~ 4 years 4 months. Light would be seen in April 1999.

4. (a) see page 20.

(b) $\lambda = \frac{v}{f} = \frac{1{,}600}{8{,}000{,}000} = 0.000\,2\text{ m} = \underline{0.2\text{ mm}}$

(c) because the wavelength of 8 MHz waves is shorter than that of 2.25 MHz waves.

(d) See page 20, 'Sound in Medicine', paragraph **5**.

(e) Ultrasound doesn't cause ionisation which can present a risk to humans.

5. (a) $\frac{1}{2}mv^2 = \frac{1}{2} \times 68{,}500 \times (93)^2 = \underline{296{,}228{,}250\text{ J}}$

(b) Change in kinetic energy = work done to stop shuttle

$$\frac{1}{2}mv^2 = Fd$$
$$296{,}228{,}250 = F \times 2{,}000$$
$$\text{hence } F = \underline{148{,}114\text{ N}}$$

(c) It becomes heat.

(d) High melting point.

Past examination questions are reproduced by kind permission of the Scottish Examination Board. Some questions have been adapted. Solutions do not emanate from the Board.